THE
MENTALLY RETARDED
CHILD

УМСТВЕННО ОТСТАЛЫЙ РЕБЕНОК

А. Р. ЛУРИЯ

THE MENTALLY RETARDED CHILD

*Essays based on a study of
the peculiarities of the
higher nervous functioning of
child-oligophrenics*

Edited by
Professor A. R. Luria

Translated from the Russian by
W. P. Robinson
Department of Psychology
University of Hull

English translation edited by
Dr. Brian Kirman

PERGAMON PRESS
OXFORD · LONDON · NEW YORK · PARIS
1963

PERGAMON PRESS LTD.
Headington Hill Hall, Oxford
4 & 5 Fitzroy Square, London W.1

PERGAMON PRESS INC.
122 East 55th Street, New York 22, N.Y.

GAUTHIER-VILLARS ED.
55 Quai des Grands-Augustins, Paris 6

PERGAMON PRESS G.m.b.H.
Kaiserstrasse 75, Frankfurt am Main

Distributed in the Western Hemisphere by
THE MACMILLAN COMPANY · NEW YORK
pursuant to a special arrangement with
Pergamon Press Limited

Copyright © 1963
Pergamon Press Ltd.

A translation of the original volume "Umstvenno otstalyi rebenok. Ocherki izucheniya osobennostei vysshei nervnoi deyatel'nosti detei-oligofrenov," under the editorship of Professor A. R. Luria and published in Moscow 1960 by the Academy of Pedagogical Sciences of the Russian Socialist Federative Soviet Republic.

Library of Congress Catalog Card No. 63–10015

Printed in Poland
PWN—DRP

CONTENTS

PREFACE

This book acquaints the reader with results obtained in recent years from the study of the clinical peculiarities and the characteristics of higher nervous functioning of mentally retarded children studying in auxiliary schools—and especially of child-oligophrenics.

Long ago Soviet science concluded that mentally retarded children (and in particular, child-oligophrenics) were children who had experienced a serious brain disease during the intra-uterine or early post-natal period of their development. This disease had disrupted their cerebral functioning and led to a gross anomaly in their mental development. Naturally a careful study of the clinical peculiarities and the characteristics of the higher nervous functioning of such children is essential.

However, although the necessity of a scientific approach to the mentally retarded child is universally acknowledged, there are no books in the literature in which the basic facts relevant to the development, the clinical characteristics, and the unique features of the higher nervous activity of the mentally retarded child, have been set out in collated and readily accessible form.

The present book has been written by a group of colleagues at the Institute of Defectology in the Academy of Pedagogical Sciences of the R.S.F.S.R. who have been studying the problems presented and this book should fill the gap in the literature mentioned.

The chapters of the book were written by the following authors: 1, 6, and 8 by A. R. Luria; 2 by M. S. Pevsner; 3 by N. N. Zislina; 4 by A. R. Luria and O. S. Vinogradov; 5 by V. I. Lubovskii; 7 by A. R. Luria, O. S. Vinogradov and A. I. Meshcheryakov.

The authors express their gratitude to G. M. Dul'ner who read through the text and made valuable comments.

The authors hope that the book will be of help to the teachers in defectology, psychiatrists and psychologists who are concerned with the problems of training, educating, and curing mentally retarded children.

A. LURIA

CHAPTER 1

THE PROBLEM OF
MENTAL RETARDATION AND ITS STUDY

AMONG the children undergoing education in ordinary schools is a group which cannot master the normal school programme because of their mental under-development. This group needs to study in special auxiliary schools. Its members are the so-called *mentally retarded* children and the problem of identifying them in time, separating them from other backward though fully normal children, and providing them with special instruction, is one of the essential tasks of a special pedagogy.

Exactly what are mentally retarded children and how can they be distinguished from other children who have been educationally neglected?

In the capitalist countries the view has been held for a long time that mentally retarded childern are normal children, but are by nature of inferior ability. It was thought that this inferior ability was inherited and applied to a large section of the child population which consequently could not be educated in ordinary schools nor receive a full education.

In order to separate this group of children in the capitalist countries, all children between ten and eleven years of age undergo short psychological tests—"tests of intellectual ability". These consist of a series of tasks requiring shrewdness and general knowledge. Those children who do well in these tasks are placed in class "A" where pupils pursue an advanced programme and later transfer to an advanced type of school. The second group, placed in the middle by the tests, are put in class "B" and the third group, with the lowest marks, are treated as having inferior abilities and put in class "C".

Pupils in this last group are considered incapable of receiving a complete education; they are sent to a lower type of school and when they finish there they cannot progress further and have to remain unqualified workers.

It is quite clear that such a system of selecting children—as though they were of "low intellectual level"—openly carries a social class bias. The system is still used in capitalist countries.* An inability to cope with set tasks requiring shrewdness and general knowledge certainly does not segregate children whose low abilities stem "from nature". It is perfectly natural that children who grow up in intellectual and well-off families obtain a better upbringing and have all the opportunities of developing shrewdness and acquiring a much wider range of general knowledge. Conversely, workers' children, whose families are not well-off, receive less attention, their knowledge is usually more limited and their speech training and intellectual activity less. Understandably, these children, with their good practical shrewdness, receive lower marks in those tasks requiring sharpness and information which make up the content of the "intellectual tests". The children of the less well-off classes of the population usually fall into class "C" and find themselves doomed to receive a low level of education, whole the well-prepared children of the better-off classes receive all the opportunities of higher education, allowing them to occupy a superior position in society in the future.

These methods of selecting children of "low ability" are wrong not only because of their class bias; they are derived from false theoretical principles.

Supporters of these methods of selection—and there are still very many of them in the capitalist countries—argue from the idea that mental retardation can be treated as a variant of abili-

---

* This system, which is used in many parts of England, is well analysed by Brian Simon in *The English School and Intelligence Tests*, Moscow, A.P.N R.S.F.S.R., 1958.

ties determined by heredity and that there is a rather large group among perfectly normal children who cannot learn in ordinary schools because of their innately low capabilities.

In this way, according to the theory, the possibilities of the subsequent development of the child do not depend on the conditions of his environment, but are predetermined from within, by the mental "capabilities" given. It is hardly possible to deny that different children have differing characteristics. Alongside the slow "phlegmatic" children are the quick "sanguine" children. Children differ in the strength, balance, and lability* of their nervous processes.

Soviet investigators have shown, however, that children of diverse temperaments easily devise individual methods of work dependent upon their particular characteristics. Among the outstanding pupils of a school, it is possible to find the slow as well as the fast, the sluggish as well as the labile, the well balanced as well as the insufficiently balanced. Under certain conditions, with properly devised methods of instruction and with the necessary diligence and systematization, even children of low natural ability can master the programme of an ordinary school without difficulty and receive an all-round and properly balanced education in the process of which his abilities form and develop still further.

A school does not so much reveal innate abilities of children as form and develop them, and every child who acquires the requisite methods and habits of study in school develops his abilities, compensates for his deficiencies, and obtains further opportunities for mental development.

The school itself has a most powerful influence on development. It would be a great mistake to underestimate its significance and to consider that "innate abilities" define the subsequent fate of children. It would be a mistake to discount those difficulties experienced by children during education as being the consequence of low inborn talent.

* These technical terms are explained later.

Among those who learn with difficulty in ordinary schools are some who experience insuperable difficulties in mastering the school programme and even after dogged efforts by the teachers are still unfit to move on to the acquisition of new techniques and knowledge. Usually these children are behind their peers in learning from the very beginning. They cannot master the school programme, cannot assimilate the necessary knowledge, and cannot understand the teacher's explanations. Their backwardness is revealed with particular clarity when the other children begin to learn abstract material. The children being discussed do not have the ability to master such material and they remain for a second year (and sometimes for a third also) in the same class, falling behind in ordinary work and disorganizing the teaching of the class.

These are *mentally retarded children* and they are sharply distinguishable from all the other unsuccessful children. The psychological study of these children permits an elucidation of the *abnormal characteristics* of their mental processes. A careful study of their developmental history usually reveals that they suffered from serious brain pathology during intrauterine or early life and this has resulted in their whole mental development remaining anomalous.

To consider these children as having "inferior talent" and regard them as normal variants, but of "low ability", would be a great mistake. In fact they are anomalous children and all their behavioural deficiences are a survival of an early disorder which has caused the under-development of the brain and serious defects of mental activity.

The peculiarities of the mental activity of these children have been well described by psychologists: their range of ideas, the distinctive characteristics of their intellectual operations and the uniqueness of their behaviour. Mentally retarded children are fundamentally different from their normal peers in all these ways.

The normal child begins to widen the scope of his orientation to the real world very early in life and to subject his sensations to complex analysis and synthesis. When he starts to walk he expands his knowledge of the perceptual world beyond the limits of the room where he has lived. When he begins to play he becomes accustomed to distinguishing different aspects of the objects in the surrounding real world. He begins to adapt the use of these objects to his intentions and to link and relate them in different ways. When he begins to learn he acquires a broad and systematic knowledge of objects and moves far beyond the boundaries of his immediate sensations. His perception of an object is affected by the knowledge he has assimilated from adults. He becomes capable of enriching his perception of objects and discovers new connections and relationships into which these objects can enter. He systematizes the objects he encounters according to various categories. His immediate perception of objects is replaced by complex processes of comparison, discrimination and generalization, analysis and synthesis.

In fact it becomes a continuous thought process dealing with things perceived.

The mentally retarded child is sharply distinguished from the normal by the range of ideas he can comprehend and by the character of his perception of reality.*

Investigations have shown that the process of perception of surrounding objects proceeds at a considerably slower rate for the mentally retarded child than for his normal peer and, as a rule, it does not extend so far beyond immediate sensations. Consequently while a normal child of Junior School age easily discriminates the diverse properties and aspects of an object, analyses it and incorporates it into various systems of connections and relation-

* The psychological characteristics of mentally retarded children are described in the following books: L. V. Zankov, *The Mentally Retarded Child*, Moscow, Uchpedgiz, 1936; L. V. Zankov. and I. I. Danyushevsky (Eds.) *Questions of the Psychology of Deaf-mute and Mentally Retarded Children*, Moscow, Uchpedgiz, 1940; I. M. Solovyev (Ed.) *Characteristics of the Cognitive Activity of Children Learning in Auxiliary Schools,* Moscow, Uchpedgiz, 1953. The most complete foreign summaries of the psychological characteristics of mentally retarded children can be found in the following books: C. Burt, *The Backward Child*, 4th ed., London, University Press, 1958; A. M. Clarke and A. B. D. Clarke (Eds.) *Mental Deficiency*, London, Methuen, 1958.

ships, the mentally retarded child perceives only the ordinary features of objects, does not discriminate their many-sided properties, and does not effect a complex analysis and synthesis of these. As a result the perceptions of mentally retarded childern are much more barren than those of their normal peers and the range of their ideas considerably more narrow and limited. Impressions of the external world are less total and more fragmented; their thinking is incomparably less systematic, much more diffuse and monotonous.*

In order to see this it is sufficient to see how a mentally retarded child describes a thematic picture and how he (as opposed to an ordinary child) only grasps the separate objects represented in it and those activities with which he is familiar. The whole richness of associations and relationships represented remains inaccessible to such a child. It is easy to see that the range of the perceptions and ideas which make up the world of a mentally retarded child is incomparably more barren and limited than that obtained by his normal peer. Similarly the types of analysis and synthesis to which he subjects his perception of reality are incomparably more fragmentary and superficial than those used by a normal child.

Closely related to what has just been said about the perceptions of a mentally retarded child are the series of important peculiarities in the dynamics of his mental activity.

Soviet psychological investigations have shown that a child's mental development is characterized by a distinct succession of separate stages, each having its unique features.

The child begins to acquire his knowledge of the world from the specific practical forms of material events. He manipulates proffered objects, feels them, and in that way orients himself in the external world. Only subsequently is speech added to this specific practical activity: {he names objects and talks about them; at first under the guidance of adults, but later independently. It is only in the last phase of this great stage in mental develop-

* These features are described at length by I. M. Solovyev in *Characteristics of the Cognitive Activity of Children Learning in Auxiliary Schools*, Moscow, Uchpedgiz, 1953.

ment that the specific practical activities of the child are curtailed and condensed, and the child begins to orient himself in the external world by means of internal activity, including verbal thought. With the help of verbal thinking he enriches the associations of his past experience and forms new associations.

This transition from specific external actions to internal or *mental actions* is one of the most important features of the mental development of a child and every normal child of just under or just over the age of school entry must succeed in passing through these basic stages.* This progress is clearly revealed in the development of the child's cognitive activities and in the gradual formation of those internal mental operations which fill his school life. It is sufficient to trace carefully the formation of the young child's concept of number. This formation begins with the specific practical examination of objects, and their external enumeration. This process gradually diminishes, the visual tracking of a whole series of objects follows and then comes external speech. We can trace the gradual reduction of the speech and the transition to the denotation of whole groups of objects by separate numbers. Finally the child masters "silent" mental reckoning, accomplished with the help of the well-known "calculation tables". When this whole complex process is adequately traced out the phases of the gradual formation of complex "mental actions" emerges with sufficient clarity.

This example of the formation of mental reckoning operations is not unique. In principle, the development of the child's reading and writing follows the same course—as does the development of motor skills and, in the last instance, his ideation.

In all these instances *the specific practical activity begins to be mediated by speech and is converted into that system of internal operations which is the most important acquisition in a child's normal mental development.*

* These stages of psychic development were described by L. S. Vygotskii in *Selected Psychological Investigations*, Moscow, A.P.N. R.S.F.S.R., 1956, and also A. N. Leont'ev, A. V. Zaporozhets, D. B. El'konin, and especially P. Ya. Gal'perin.

8   THE MENTALLY RETARDED CHILD

The formation of the mental processes of mentally retarded children is utterly different.

Mental retardation is not apparent in all the developmental stages. When the child's activity has a sufficiently simple and specific character it is not apparent. It begins to appear quite clearly, however, as soon as the normal child starts to develop internal modes of cognitive activity and switches to internal intellectual operations mediated by speech. Under these circumstances the inadequacy of the mentally retarded child is fully apparent. The mentally retarded child can easily sort and can sometimes enumerate objects displayed before him, but to notice his defects it is only necessary to propose that he solve arithmetical problems working in his head alone—mentally adding the numbers given. As a rule the mentally retarded child proves quite helpless, regresses to specific actions associated with enumeration or solves the problem posed by counting on his fingers. It is only possible to convert him from external enumeration to real internal counting after considerable effort—sometimes lasting for years. Often, in the more severe types of mental retardation, even prolonged training does not lead to the required success: the abbreviated mental operations do not develop and neither does the thinking, [which is] a necessary condition of such operations. The activities of the child remain at the level of specific external actions. Consequently many experienced teachers who wish to verify the extent of the development of a mentally retarded child ask him to do tasks in mental reckoning. If an unsuccessful school child has remained in a particular class for a long time and continues to carry out these operations with the aid of external enumeration, he can certainly be assigned to the class of mentally retarded children.

A delay in the formation of internal operations of synthesis can certainly be viewed as one of the outstanding characteristics of the mentally retarded child. This delay appears in his ideas and in his knowledge and is closely connected to *backwardness of speech*, and those complex systems of associations which are formed on the basis of speech.

The mental backwardness of these children is also revealed

in their examination of pictures, in their comprehension of arithmetical tasks, in their assimilation of a complex text and in their development of abstract understanding. In all these situations the mentally retarded child only grasps the most obvious fragments, does not synthesize these, nor create a preliminary system of connections which would enable understanding of the arithmetical task, text, or concepts.

This characteristic of the mentally retarded child is closely related to the underdevelopment of the sense of his speech, which often remains for a long time at the level of naming separate objects or common activities. For him speech does not serve as a foundation for new associations and relationships, but more as a means of reproducing prepared clichés and habitual recollections.

Hence the fact that when he has assimilated some rule, the mentally retarded child can apply it under new conditions only with considerable difficulty and can only accomplish the operation of *transfer of experience*, on which school instruction is based, very laboriously.

The narrowness of orientation, the poverty of analysis and synthesis, the backwardness of the complex mediated forms of cognitive activity and the inability to transfer to these types of "mental" actions—all these differentiate between the mentally retarded child and his normal peer even though the latter may only be progressing with difficulty.

Teachers often complain of the great defects in "attention" of mentally retarded children and of their inability to concentrate for very long on any task they are given. They point out that frequently such children obey verbal instructions and finish their work without any digression only with great difficulty. Often an insignificant noise in the corridor such as an opening door or a bird flapping at the window distracts these children so much that only the experienced teacher can re-direct attention to the lesson.

Frequently teachers note the great "tiredness" of some of these children. If they have worked hard for ten or fifteen minutes they quickly become weary, cease to understand questions addressed to them and sometimes begin to show restlessness and obstinacy They make a noise, are distracted by extraneous conversations, sometimes they even become listless and indifferent, and they cease to answer questions almost completely. In these ways as well they strongly contrast with normal school children, who only tire after a much longer period and do not disrupt their activities in such ways.

In addition teachers draw attention to the significant lack of good behaviour of mentally retarded children. Some of these children are negativistic and oppose every attempt to direct their behaviour or they use their energy to carry out some task other than the one prescribed. Some do not adopt the norms of behaviour which ought to characterize a child in school; they behave similarly in class, during the change-over of lessons and towards their teachers and comrades. They do not feel concerned with the bad marks they receive, are not sensitive to their comrades, and are not pleased by their own successes. All these peculiarities of mentally retarded children's behaviour reveal the strong eccentricity of the development of their personality. As with the peculiarities of their cognitive activity, so these peculiarities clearly separate them from normal school children.

Psychological investigations give a clear description of mentally retarded children and the peculiarities of their mental development. On the other hand it remains unclear how the appearance of such peculiarities are to be explained. Why are these children so different from the mass of children in ordinary schools?

Perhaps there can only be one answer to that question.

As we have seen above mentally retarded children are not normal children and the defects in their cognitive activity and in their behaviour are not simply common insufficiencies of "talent" or of character.

Mentally retarded children—or oligophrenics as the doctors call them (from the Greek words "oligo"—small, "phrenos"—mind)—have suffered from a severe brain disease while in the uterus or in early childhood and this has disturbed the normal development of the brain and produced serious anomalies in mental development. In consequence all these peculiarities of their mental functioning and behaviour which we have observed are not the result of a natural diversity of individual characteristics, but are the result of a severe disease which they have endured. Its consequence is an anomalous development of brain functioning.

This conception of mental retardation forces the readoption of a scientific analysis of those characteristics peculiar to the cognitive activity and behaviour of the mentally retarded child. The existence of a serious brain injury as the source of the anomalous mental development demands a careful description of *the causes and clinical* forms of those diseases which produced this anomalous development and an analysis of *those peculiarities of the physiology of the higher nervous functions* characteristic of an injured brain. *We can understand the psychological disturbances (described by teachers) which are the distinctive features of mental retardation, only through a careful study of the clinically and pathologically changed nervous activity of the child.*

The clinical–physiological analysis of the symptoms of mental retardation and the establishment of a defectology founded in natural science is one of the most important tasks of the pedagogical science concerned with mental retardation.

Lately scientific medicine, and Soviet physiology in particular, have achieved significant successes and have done what was possible to give a scientific explanation of much that had previously only been described subjectively and had not been explained in the necessary way.

Through the study of early diseases in foetuses (which derive from inflammatory conditions, traumatic, toxic, and parasitic factors), and through an analysis of the consequences of ancestral traumata and diseases of early childhood, clinical medicine has been able to establish the real source of many aspects of mental retardation which were previously obscure. In describing such factors as the under-development of the brain and its delicate structure, the appearance of fluid in the brain as a result of inflammation, clinical medicine was able to expose a series of conditions which can lead to a pathological development of neural connections and can complicate normal brain functions. Clinicians discovered those pathological features of children's behaviour whose causes were hitherto unknown, by relying on the latest achievements of physiology and particularly those of contemporary electro-physiology.

Such considerations have enabled a significant expansion of our knowledge of the mentally retarded child and his anomalous development.

The achievements of modern physiology and the pathology of higher nervous functions had great importance in the discovery of the mechanisms fundamental to a child's anomalous development. These disciplines established the basis of those changes of the mental activity of the mentally retarded child in terms of natural science— a problem which had long disconcerted the pedagogue.

When I. P. Pavlov—the initiator of modern scientific work on the brain—studied the functions of the cerebral hemispheres in animals' brains by the method of conditioned reflexes, he showed that the primary functions of these hemispheres was to analyse and synthesize the stimuli which an organism receives from the external world and to construct circuits of new temporary connections by which the organism can adapt to the changing conditions of its environment. The higher the animal is on the evolutionary scale, the more complex the analysis and synthesis of external stimuli and the richer and more varied the network of temporary connections.

Both the mentioned processes are basic aspects of the activity of the human brain. As opposed to animals, social man is exposed to abstract and social signals as well as to the common mediated signals of reality. These are contained in *language* and constitute "the second signalling system of reality". The existence of this system immeasurably complicates the activity of the human brain and creates a basis for the assimilation of experience common to all mankind and for the development of those higher forms of mental life which are the inalienable essence of man.

The normal continuation of the main types of brain activity is only possible when certain necessary conditions are met. The continual flow requires a sufficient *strength* of nervous processes, their *balance* and high *lability*.

If the *strength* of nervous processes diminishes (as for example when one is tired, when the brain contains toxins, or when the organism is generally weak) the brain cannot maintain the necessary level of excitation in the nerve cells nor the necessary intensity of inhibitory processes. The excitation which arises in the cortex on the reception of each signal ceases to be specific and becomes diffusely distributed over the neural elements. This weakness of the basic nervous processes (excitation and inhibition) is fundamental to the disordered spreading of associations which we observe in ourselves when we are very tired or ill, or when we are just falling off to sleep. In this instance the internal inhibition, which orders the flow of associations and preserves their organized and systematic character, has weakened and every irrelevant stimulus easily distracts and destroys the normal flow of mental processes.

These deficiencies are especially evident when the cortex is in a particular pathological state, called inhibited or "phasic"; arising from a pathological decrement in the strength of the nervous processes. Under these circumstances the basic action of stimuli is perverted. Strong stimuli acting on a weakened brain inhibit the cortex, while weak stimuli begin to have unexpectedly strong effects. This is why the occurrence of the unexpected "paradoxical" reactions frequently observed in anomalous behaviour is related to these "phasic" conditions.

Significant departures from normal behaviour occur when any pathological factor disrupts the normal *balance* of the basic nervous processes of excitation and inhibition. If the excitatory processes are particularly affected the person becomes listless, exhausted, and easily inhibited: he quickly ceases to respond to presented stimuli and readily falls into an inhibitory condition. If, on the other hand, the inhibitory processes are affected, his behaviour becomes restless, excited, poorly controlled and impulsive. Many facts of anomalous behaviour long considered as signs of caprice

or negativism in a child often result from a disruption of the normal
balance of the basic nervous processes.

A disturbance of the *lability* of the nervous processes evokes
substantial changes in behaviour. Normally the cortical nervous
processes are exceptionally labile. They easily switch from a state
of excitation to one of inhibition. The arousal of certain systems
of connections can be replaced by the arousal of other systems
with extraordinary speed. Every function of the cerebral hemispheres depends on the "dynamic mosaic of excited and inhibited
loci" and if this mosaic does not possess a high lability, no normal
mental activity requiring quick changes in various systems of connections is possible. However, it is precisely the lability of nervous
processes which may be disrupted in pathological brain conditions.
It is sufficient for the normal state of the brain to have been disturbed by trauma, tumour, excess fluid or increased intracranial pressure can be shown by the depressed lability of the nervous processes
in the injured parts. Physiologists call this depressed lability pathological inertness. If an aroused excited condition does not dissipate
nor change to an inhibited one or if an aroused wave of inhibition
stabilizes, the brain cannot switch quickly from one system of
connections to another. The same applies when a developed system
of connections "sticks" for a long time in a pathologically changed
brain. A reduction of the lability of the nervous processes and
the pathological inertness can characterize any pathological brain
condition and can lead to unique "fixated" forms of behaviour.
As we shall see below, many behavioural peculiarities of mentally
retarded children are explained by their possession of an injured
brain whose nervous processes have lost "lability" and have begun
to acquire the characteristics of unusual pathological inertness.

We have only noted some of the basic features typifying the
physiological changes occurring in pathological conditions of the
brain, but they enable us to see with full clarity, how substantial
disturbances of mental activity can develop under such circumstances.

It is easy to see that the loss of strength, balance, and lability
of the basic nervous processes prevents the brain from achieving

complex analytic–synthetic activities and from establishing complex systems of temporary connections. This loss leads to links which are formed, being unstable while all incidental influences disrupt the complex systems reduce the efficiency of the cerebral cortex and render the connections which are being established, fragmentary and inflexible. These pathological conditions destroy the possibility of the participation of speech in the organization of mental processes and speech is the basis of the more complex connections of the second signalling system. The involvement of complex speech connections requires particular balance and lability of the nervous processes and each disturbance of these makes the formation of this second complex system of connections impossible.

Consequently a careful analysis of changes in the higher nervous processes facilitates an approach to the scientific basis of anomalous behaviour and an opportunity to produce a scientific description of the causal mechanisms involved. The purpose of this book is to provide a short exposition of data obtained, relevant to this issue.*

We will not have explained with sufficient fullness all the basic problems associated with a scientific approach to anomalous behaviour in general and that of mentally retarded children in particular, if we do not pause for a moment. Any lack of clear understanding renders the approach insecure.

The disturbances of brain activity which we have discussed and whose significance for an understanding of the causes and physiological mechanisms of mental activities has been stressed, occur in early childhood—in the very first stages of development. This circumstance distinguishes the disruptions described from

---

* The clinical characteristics and peculiarities of the higher nervous activity of mentally retarded children are described in detail in a series of books among which we may mention: A. R. Luria (Ed.), *Problems in the Higher Nervous Activity of Normal and Abnormal Children*, Moscow, A.P.N. R.S.F.S.R., Vol. 1. 1956, Vol. 2. 1958; E. N. Pravdina-Vinarskaya, *Neurological Characteristics of the Oligophrenic Syndrome*, Moscow, A.P.N. R.S.F.S.R., 1957; M. S. Pevsner, *Child Oligophrenics*, Moscow, A.P.N. R.S.F.S.R., 1959.

those which arise later, in a brain which has already achieved full complexity and maturity.

In actual fact the brain injuries which subsequently provoke mental retardation *remove the healthy foundation of all future development*. If the disturbances are sufficiently massive and are associated with those aspects of mental activity which are necessary to establish normal mental processes, they inevitably result in a retarded or anomalous formation of all the more complex aspects of intellectual functioning.

Just one example will show how much greater the consequences are when such an injury to normal mental functioning occurs in early childhood rather than in adulthood.

The occipital areas of the brain are the primary mediating centres for visual experience. It is known that injuries to these areas can occur in adults (as a result of wounds, tumours, or haemorrhage) as well as in children. But the results of such injuries are quite different in the two cases.

Clinicians are well aware of the consequences of injuries to the occipital (visual) cortex in the adult. Such a person loses the power to perceive clearly and to analyse visual stimuli; he cannot immediately perceive any visual representation nor the whole of a complex picture; he confuses the direction of lines and is unable to read. However, auditory and tactual analysis and synthesis are preserved. He can still write and can sometimes compensate for visual deficiency by tracing the outline of letters by hand or by eye. Of prime significance, however, is the fact that such a person retains the power of speech and of abstract understanding so that whenever he experiences difficulties with a visual analysis of objects he can bring his reasoning to bear on the matter.

A completely different picture is presented by the child who has suffered injuries to the occipital areas of the cerebral hemispheres in the earliest stages of his development. In contrast to the blind man he does not only lose the afferent visual stimulation from the external world. The very apparatus is disrupted which enables the submission of such stimulation to analysis and synthesis and its storage in a systematized manner (this central apparatus is preserved in the blinded man). Consequently the ability to reflect the external world in an orderly manner, to compare and analyse it, to receive a synthesized picture of the world of external objects in which the child lives, are all destroyed. The final effect follows from this. If the perceptual world of the child remains unorganized, the speech which ordinarily develops on a foundation of clear and continuous visual perceptions, cannot develop properly. The speech of the child for whom words acquired in communication do not develop on the firm basis of concrete perception becomes empty and devoid of the necessary content. The result is that all his thinking and the suitability of his behaviour is under-developed. In sum even a small locus of injury which disrupts the normal function of those processes necessary for future mental development leads to a delay and disturbance of development with the consequence that the child's mental life is far more barren than it might have been.

Hence in the child and adult one and the same brain injury leads to very different results and the consequences for the child depend to a considerable extent not only on the severity of the injury, but on the developmental stage at which it occurred and the precise systems which it initially destroys. To appreciate *the importance which brain injury has for the future development of a child, it is necessary to refract the appraisal of the results of brain injury through the prism of development* and this is one of the most vital conditions of a successful scientific analysis of those types of anomalies which arise out of brain injuries in children. Later we will attempt to show the significance of earlier disruption of the dynamics of the higher nervous processes.

*　　*

*

In a general way we have traced the role played by scientific analysis towards an understanding of mental retardation. This analysis was based on clinical investigations and on the study of the characteristics of pathologically changed higher nervous activity. We can' add that such an analysis substantially facilitates the recognition of children who belong to the category of the mentally retarded and facilitates the working out of compensatory techniques to assist, if only partially, in their training, upbringing, and in the mastery of their defects.

We would like to dwell still further on the subject of the significance of the clinical approach for the resolution of a basic problem—the working out of a differential approach to the various groups of retarded children.

Mentally retarded children, subject to transfer to auxiliary schools, are only a comparatively small group among the children who learn in ordinary schools and experience difficulties in coping with the school programme. It is very necessary therefore to separate them from those other unsuccessful children with whom this book is not concerned. These children must be described briefly.

When we are trying to study mentally retarded children, we must separate them sharply from at least three groups which make up the large majority of unsuccessful children in ordinary schools. The *first* such group comprises those children who are normal, but have been *pedagogically neglected* for some reason. Because of certain circumstances they have not acquired the necessary knowledge or experience, they have ceased to keep pace with the class and have fallen out of the general stream of learning. The reasons for any given child being pedagogically neglected and backward can be very varied. There are children in this group who for some reason (e.g. an infection with subsequent quarantine) did not come to school for a long time and did not learn those methods and skills (e.g. skills of reckoning) which their fellow school children did master. If these children are not given sufficient individual instruction they frequently appear quite helpless. Not knowing the necessary methods, they begin to lag behind the class. At first they make efforts to catch up, but then they despair and become "intellectually-passive" children. These make up a large part of the group of unsuccessful children.

Also in this group are those children for whom a lack of desire to learn has arisen as a result of an affective conflict with a teacher, a class, or the family. Some of these lose the necessary self-confidence when they experience failure. and they incorrectly begin to be persuaded of their incapability or experience a long affective conflict and cease to study actively.

These children have nothing in common with mentally retarded children. They need individual assistance and ought to continue to study in ordinary schools.*

In the *second* group of unsuccessful children—also not mentally retarded—are those with normal brains, but *with partial and peripheral defects*. The great majority of these have *defective hearing*.

Normal hearing is one of the most important conditions of a full mental development. Only when a child has normal hearing (a sense finely developed in man) can he correctly discriminate between sounds, differentiate words, and assimilate the logico-grammatical structure of language. If therefore the hearing is destroyed from birth (and this frequently occurs as a result of a bilateral suppurating inflammation of the middle ear, neuritis in the auditory nerve, and other causes), the child cannot follow the speech of others properly and he cannot clearly discriminate the sounds which make up speech. He can understand neither individual words nor complex turns of speech. *Many children are unable to master correct* speech because of defects in hearing and very many of them begin to experience great difficulties when they learn to write.

Such a lack of oral communication with others cannot avoid producing a natural retardation in intellectual development, and whilst, with respect to their capabilities, such children remain normal, they begin to lag in the development of verbal thought and do not succeed in school.

Such children need to transfer to special schools for children with defective hearing where special methods are used to instruct them. These methods facilitate their speech development and insure normal intellectual development.

We can also mention the *third* group of children in normal schools who are unsuccessful, but not mentally retarded. These

---

* Methods of individual work with such children are described in a book by L. S. Slavnaya, *The Individual Approach to the Unsuccessful and Undisciplined Child Pupil*, Moscow, A.P.N. R.S.F.S.R., 1958.

are the *feeble* or *asthenic* children. Some of these have suffered from an infectious disease, others from brain traumata and others from prolonged dystrophia. All these children have normal brains and learn successfully, but are considerably hindered by their pronounced susceptibility to exhaustion. Usually they can assimilate material well over a short period, but they cannot maintain the tempo of the class and after ten or fifteen minutes are so exhausted that they cease to absorb what they are given to do and become incapable of carrying out any complex intellectual activity. In some children the exhaustion manifests itself as listlessness or sleepiness and in others as distractability. From no point of view can they be accounted as mentally retarded, but instruction under ordinary school conditions is beyond their strength.

Such children ought to be trained under special conditions— in schools for neurally weak children—where the regime, composition of the class and the programme of instruction is specially arranged to provide a course which is within their grasp and does not evoke the severe conflicts which inevitably arise if children are presented with impossible demands.

The study of all these children, who make up the majority of unsuccessful children in ordinary schools, does not enter into the plan of this book. In the following pages we concentrate our attention entirely on the characteristics of mentally retarded children (child-oligophrenics). These form the most severely affected group and have suffered an early brain injury leading to an anomalous development of mental activity. They need to be instructed under the special conditions of an *auxiliary school*.

Since we are aware of the great importance which the scientific method of study has for an understanding of the causes of underdevelopment and of the mechanism of defective behaviour, we will first study the *clinical* characteristics of these children, and then elucidate the peculiarities of their nervous activity revealed in both *physiological* and *psycho-physiological* study.

The exposition of the basic data gathered in recent years through a scientific study of mentally retarded children comprises the task of this book.

CHAPTER 2

THE CLINICAL CHARACTERISTICS OF MENTALLY RETARDED CHILDREN—CHILD-OLIGOPHRENICS

1. *Causes of Oligophrenia*

Initially we will be concerned with the peculiarities of the higher nervous activity of mentally retarded children. We will point out its distinctive features and reveal what has been found out about these children from clinical study.

Most mentally retarded children who are directed to special schools are known in clinics as child-oligophrenics. As we have shown above, these children have suffered from a serious brain disease either while in the uterus or during early childhood, and this has changed the brain tissue and disrupted the higher nervous processes. Typical in these children is a disruption of general mental development, which has become anomalous and has prevented the children from mastering complex forms of cognitive activity connected with abstraction and generalization.

Many writers interested in mental retardation have been inclined to widen the concept of oligophrenia drastically. Frequently different types of feeblemindedness in children have been included in the group of the feebleminded and intellectually deficient oligophrenics. Often mental retardation resulting from epileptic processes, traumata, or schizophrenia have been included, along with those types of feeblemindedness consequent upon an organic brain injury incurred in the late stages of a child's development. As we have stated above, the broadening of the concept of oligophrenia also occurs because children who are unsuccessful in ordinary schools

21

for diverse reasons are inappropriately put into this category — although they are by no means truly oligophrenic.

The technical term "mentally retarded children" as it occurs in pedagogical and defectological practice in fact conceals a tendency to refer clinically diverse syndromes to one category.

If we are to approach the problem of mental retardation scientifically, we must narrow the concept of oligophrenia considerably and discriminate between it and other conditions which are only superficially similar.

Questions of the origin (aetiology and pathogenesis), of the fundamental physiological mechanisms involved in the symptomatology and the classification of types of oligophrenia have remained debatable.

There have been different points of view regarding the origin of oligophrenia. Some writers have attached critical significance to heredity. Others have correctly pointed out that oligophrenic feeblemindedness has the same symptoms of brain injury as aphasia, apraxia, and apoplexy and that the study of it requires a consideration of the time when the injury occurred and its locus. Recently scientists have talked less and less of the inherited nature of oligophrenia and more of them are beginning to accept the view that it derives from some external pathological factors which disrupt the normal development of the brain.

Very recently work has appeared which demonstrates that oligophrenia can result from the effects of infection, intoxication, or a disturbance of the metabolism of the developing foetal brain.

It is known that the pregnant mother developing German measles can result in a disturbance of the normal development of the foetal brain. Changes in metabolism (e.g. when the metabolism of amino-acids—phenylalanine, is disrupted) can have the same effect. Finally, in some cases, certain parasites (known as *toxoplasma*) can disrupt the brain and cause oligophrenia. Oligophrenia can result from other pathological conditions of intra-uterine development. Very frequently the normal development of the brain is disrupted by trauma affecting the brain during parturition—for instance cases of incorrect forceps deliveries leading to cerebral haemorrhage or prolonged asphyxia of a child etc. In addition there have been cases where a very young child has suffered from intoxication evoked by chronic dyspepsia or has undergone trauma in the first months of life and been diagnosed as oligophrenic.

The investigations we have pursued of a considerable number of child-oligophrenics show that oligophrenia either arises from an injury to the embryonic foetus, or from an injury to the central nervous system in the early developmental stages of a child, and anatomical changes in brain structure are basic to the problem.

The *pathological anatomy* in oligophrenia has not been sufficiently studied up until now. Usually two types of anatomical changes are noticeable in the oligophrenic. One is characterized by underdevelopment of the brain (an inadequate development of the convolutions, a reduced number of cortical layers, an incorrect distribution of cells in these layers, a small number of nerve cells, an underdevelopment of the white matter, the appearance of cellular elements in the white matter, etc.).

When organic lesions have arisen in the later foetal stages or in the early period of the child's life, the anatomical changes may have a somewhat different character. In these cases various effects can be observed: a thickening of the cerebral membranes; the soft cerebral membranes becoming united to the nervous tissue, sometimes foci of sclerotic overgrowth, cysts, or focalized and diffuse atrophy. In the majority of examinations, residual hydrocephalus, evoked by a disturbance of the normal outflow of cerebral fluid as a result of the union of cerebral membranes with the nervous tissues, is observed. The copious fluid accumulates in the submembranous spaces and produces an expansion of the ventricles and renders the further development of nerve cells pathological.

There is an indication among the anatomical examinations made, that in spite of the cortical lesions, the cerebellum, brain stem, and spinal cord of child oligophrenics can remain unaffected.

It is necessary to point out that the pathological anatomical data given mainly refer only to the more severe degrees of oligophrenia.

The changes produced by the pathological process are fine in the lesser forms of oligophrenia and are frequently discovered only upon a careful microscopic examinations of the cortex.

Naturally these gross changes in the structure of the nervous tissue of child-oligophrenics invariably evoke *changes in higher nervous activity* and lead to a *significant disturbance of the normal development of the functions of the cerebral hemispheres.* As a result of this it is clear that the whole behaviour of the child-oligophrenic will be disrupted. But in particular, the cognitive processes are underdeveloped and these processes are associated with the complex aspects of speech activity and with abstraction and generalization. The pathological change in the child-oligophrenic's brain leads to a gross disruption of his mental development.

The peculiarities of higher nervous activity of child-oligophrenics, produced by the pathological condition of the brain, will be examined in detail in succeeding chapters. Therefore we will not discuss them here.

Here we will only mention briefly the basic details which characterize the mental activity of the oligophrenic, his behaviour, and his cognitive processes.

Such an examination will enable us to present the general characteristics of the child-oligophrenic better, and will enable us to discriminate this child from children with other forms of underdevelopment. It will facilitate a more comprehensible analysis of those disturbances in the higher nervous activity of the child-oligophrenic, which lie at the basis of these changes.

2. Peculiarities of Behaviour of Oligophrenics at School

Usually even simple observation of child-oligophrenics in the early stages of their development permits us to see that they develop differently from their normal peers.

In very many cases the delayed development of the more important functions characteristic of the child is evident at a very young and pre-school age. Often they begin to *walk* later than other children and in the majority of cases they *begin to master speech* considerably later. It is not only this later development of speech but also the extremely slow tempo of development which is characteristic of child-oligophrenics. The majority of them are distinguished by poor articulation and poor vocabulary at the beginning of their school education. From the very first stage of instruction they show a deficient understanding of speech addressed to them. These children can understand straightforward speech, but not speech which is grammatically more complex and which is not accompanied by elucidatory actions.

Their *play* exhibits considerable disturbances and when they reach pre-school age these manifest defects become even more pronounced. Their games are very primitive and stereotyped. In extreme forms of oligophrenia pre-school children hardly play at all and are only slightly interested in games and dolls. When they are drawn into a play situation they cannot always adopt the expected role because of their deficient understanding of the situation.

Disturbance in play activities explains in turn the more obvious disturbance of these children when they reach school age. It is for this reason that defects of mental development emerge more sharply when these children reach school age and reveal a total lack of competence when confronted with new demands.

School age is also distinguished by a series of characteristics which did not occur in earlier developmental stages and which demand from the child completely new types of mental functioning.

It is frequently said—and with justification—that the pre-school child develops in the course of playing and interacting with those around him and conforms to any precise programme only to an insignificant extent. The child of school age finds himself in circumstances where he needs to study according to a strict programme prescribed by the teacher. This means that the child must not behave in accordance with the dictates of his personal motives and needs, but must carry out the orders of the teacher, and follow his spoken instructions all the time. He must remain within the limits set by the instructions given him and must not allow his attention to wander on to irrelevant things. Psychologically speaking this means that *all the motives behind the activities of the child who has just attained school age must be re-organized*, so that the basic motive influencing behaviour during lesson time must become "the directions of the teacher".

The contents of the child's activity change fundamentally when he reaches school-age. In the kindergarten the main ingredient of activity is playing and the child does not go beyond the simple, visual, practical activities such as building toy houses, playing fathers and mothers, getting used to looking after himself at meals and similar things. School age brings with it a substantial change. Then, types of behaviour impinge upon the child's activity which have no immediate rationale and which only derive their significance as activities which serve to prepare for new skills and habits acquired later on.

For instance, among these activities are: the disjunctive repetition of the word sounds which are subsequently necessary for learning to read and write; exercise in drawing lines and loops which are meaningful only as elements in the mastery of writing letters. It is similar with the acts of counting objects; in other words, the designation of objects (sometimes even diverse objects by the conventional numerical denominations).

Briefly almost the whole content of the first year (or even the first years) of school instruction is like this and is so very different from the content of the activity of the pre-school child.

For the transition to this new type of behaviour the child must turn away from what he has been used to; he must inhibit his direct attitude to things as being objects of practical life or play and must switch to a "school" attitude (at least to some extent). This attitude constitutes a specific and unique feature of school education.

The following feature which is connected with the transition to this new type of attitude and activity is also characteristic of the school child—it shows the special features of his *cognitive processes*. School demands from the child incomparably more complicated processes of abstraction and generalization than was typical of his *cognition* before school.

The pre-school child rides a rocking horse, feeds it with imaginary "grain"; his toy dog guards the house and when necessary it "barks"; his little toy knife "cuts"; soup is "poured" into the plate—in short everything is included in the mock visual situation as it is included in real life.

In school the child must act quite differently. He needs to discriminate the parts of the body of the horse and dog and must be able to point out the tail, head, mane, hooves or claws, teeth and fur. He has to combine the dog, horse and wolf and call them "animals". He needs to understand that the plate, cup and saucer are "crockery" and that the hammer, scissors and hand-saw are "instruments".

Later he will realize that things which look very diverse and are never seen together can be members of the same class of things, yet things occurring in one familiar situation can be members of different classes and of different abstract categories. Briefly, in place of his simple visual concrete mode of thinking evolved from the familiar real life situation he must develop a mode of thought based on abstraction and generalization, a mode of thinking in which analysis and synthesis are achieved as the basis of a preliminary abstraction of signs, a mode of thinking requiring cortical re-organization instead of the earlier consolidated direct and practical relationships to the world.

We would not have described the processes of transition to school-age adequately if we had not discussed subsequent characteristics related to the very structure of the child's mental operations.

The child of pre-school age achieves most operations directly, responding to tasks placed before him by overt acts. The child of school age achieves most operations by using the methods mastered in school, or that is, *indirectly*. As a rule these methods have, at first, an overt character, and are only subsequently abbreviated, taking on the character of mental acts. But in the majority of mental operations the mediate structure remains. At first the child counts each unit on his fingers; then he changes to the pronouncing of the separate numbers to himself, and finally to mental reckoning achieved with the help of the well-known "calculating table". At first the child writes by breaking up each enunciated word aloud into its separate sounds and writes down each element of a letter in isolation. Subsequently this operation is abbreviated, but as before, it is mediated by a whole series of covert links. All more complex intellectual processes, which at first glance seem only direct, are in fact structurally complex, and are simply abbreviated mental operations. The indirect abbreviated character of mental actions, of which the basis is internal speech, constitutes one of the fundamental features of the psychology of the school child.

Everyone knows with what ease the normal school child copes with the re-organization of behaviour and with the formation of new and complex "mental acts". Can the mentally retarded child also cope with this problem easily? Can he switch with similar ease to operations requiring, not an immediate and practical, but an abstract and theoretical relationship to things in the external world, and which are structured as complex and indirect "mental acts"?

Even the most immediate observations enable us to see that this is not so and that the defects of the child-oligophrenic, partially apparent during the infantile and pre-school period, emerge with full clarity just as soon as he is placed in front of problems which necessitate that complex form of functioning which includes subordination to the teacher's standards, the new motives, and the abstract and indirect forms of functioning which are typical for the child of school age.

It is only rarely that a child-oligophrenic is able to re-organize the habitual forms of behaviour developed during pre-school age and to confine these to the demands of the teacher, when he enters school.

As distinct from his normal peers he does not take part with the necessary alacrity in school work and may not ever begin to carry out tasks set by the teacher, sitting passively in the class, whilst his peers are actively carrying out new, although not yet fully understood, demands, or he may easily stop carrying them out and return to them only upon additional oft repeated demands by the teacher.

In the more clearly pronounced types of feeblemindedness the child does not exhibit a stable attitude to a task, does not fixate on it, and frequently switches to manipulation of the didactic material given to him. These children often do not visually fixate a letter, number, or picture shown to them, and do not listen to the explanations of the teacher. If the child is given an exercise book and pencil and is asked to do some task, for example, to describe circles, to draw or colour something, then he does not accept these tasks, but begins to sketch on the pages or tear and scrawl over the book.

The problem of assimilating new, abstract types of school tasks is a real difficulty for the child-oligophrenic. His normal peers can enter easily into the execution of tasks, associated with the analysis of a word into its constituent phonetic elements and with the preparatory stages for writing and arithmetic. They perceive the connection with future activity without difficulty and treat these tasks as elements of wider intellectual tasks. On the other hand the child-oligophrenic is most frequently not in a position to establish new connections or to comprehend the activity he is performing so that this activity immediately turns into a mechanical execution of the teacher's demands and has no kind of significance.

The mechanical character of the school activity of the child-oligophrenic and its fragmental character which is connected with his incapacity to master new themes, emerge even during the early stages of mastering reading, writing and arithmetic.

Child-oligophrenics can familiarize themselves with ordinal enumeration to the extent of the first ten numbers without particular difficulty. They can count through the series as far as ten with ease, but comprehend the quantitative nature of a number with difficulty, and they cannot separate out a given number from a group of similar terms. Instructing them to solve the most simple examples of addition and subtraction with the help of arithmetical material presents very great difficulties. They differentiate poorly between the arithmetical signs "+" and "—", confusing their names and the significance of the operations associated with them.

If the mechanical and unintelligent character of the school functioning of the child-oligophrenic appears sufficiently early— during the acquisition of the very first school habits—then the further he progresses with the school programme and the more he manages to transfer to the more complex aspects of school work which require abstraction and generalization acting in a major role and which presuppose the utilization of auxiliary, indirect operations, the greater the extent to which the incapacity of the child is revealed.

We will limit ourselves to two groups of examples only, which clearly demonstrate the nature of the difficulties experienced by such a child. The first will be taken from an analysis of arithmetical operations and lessons set aside for the solution of problems, the second from those school operations associated with the acquisition of concepts, with similarities and differences of objects, with their classification and inclusion in abstract categories.

It is well known that the normal child masters elementary arithmetical operations easily and that these are abbreviated and replaced by internal mental reckoning, operating on whole numerical groups and performing with the help of the "calculating table". The teacher is well aware of the difficulties which transition to such operations as division presents to the normal child. This requires the mastery of the abstract concept of "parts" and the abstract expression "how many times smaller", but he achieves these operations easily and begins to carry these ideas into practice after only a short time.

With the mentally retarded child this is quite different. As a rule the mentally retarded child masters successive ordinal enumeration and counting of the required number of items on his fingers relatively easily. What insuperable difficulties arise for him as soon as he has to transfer to abbreviated mental reckoning! The abandonment of counting on the fingers and the mastery of methods of reckoning with whole groups (of numbers) constituting the basis of reckoning "in the mind" is frequently an impossible task for him. Teachers in special schools well know that this transition proves so difficult that often pupils in the fourth and fifth classes in special schools continue to count with the aid of their fingers and achieve all the operations of addition and subtraction by amazingly fast movements of the fingers—but they still do not master methods of reckoning by means of numerical groups.

The difficulties which the mentally retarded child exhibits stand out even more clearly when he is solving arithmetical problems. When he is solving arithmetical problems, the child must first of all accept the conditions* proposed by the teachers; he must assimilate that system of connections which is contained in the task and must operate strictly within the limits of these connections; he must not violate them with spontaneously arising guesses, nor piecemeal operations which go outside the stipulated limits. Very often in such problems consisting of two operations he must be able to *pose* additional questions to himself which are not explicitly formulated. If in the conditions it is stated that one boy has four pencils, and another has one more, and the question asks how many pencils have the pair—he must first formulate independently the intermediate question and find out how many pencils the second child has and then proceed to the solution of the whole problem.

Teachers know what sorts of obstacles arise for the normal child who has to solve similar problems. However, they also know how successfully he masters this process, with what ease he can repeat the conditions of the problem and how easily he becomes habituated to accomplishing these operations within the conditions. He knows that the additional implicit questions can be separated out by the child and that he can return to the basic operations subsequently when the supplementary data has been obtained.

The process of solving problems proceeds quite differently with the schoolchild-oligophrenic who is not able to complete the *ad-*

---

* The word "condition" is used to refer to the parameters of mathematical problems, the constituent elements defining the problem.

ditional necessary preliminary operations of abstraction which acquire their sense only from the system of operations of the whole.

Child-oligophrenics are frequently unable to understand the task set them and accept it as a simple arithmetical example. They operate with the numbers, say the answer, but completely fail to understand the meaning structure as a whole. In one of our observations a child-oligophrenic was given a task with the following content:

Kolya had 2 pencils. His mother bought him two more pencils. How many pencils did Kolya then have?

The boy quickly calculated and answered "4". But to the question, "From whom were the four received?" he answered, "From Kolya."

Experiments involving overt repetition by the child of the conditions of a problem show the difficulties of comprehension sufficiently clearly. In such circumstances the mentally retarded child reproduces only an individual fragment of the whole set of conditions. Most frequently of all the child simplifies the conditions of the problem given to him. Stereotyped associations arise and hinder the reiteration of the problem. These associations have been firmly established in the past experience of the child.

If, for example, child-oligophrenics have previously solved simple problems, in which the arrival at "the unknown quantity" was well-prepared by the data of the problem itself, then on the transition to somewhat more complex problems they usually alter the conditions to the form of those problems previously solved.

For example, if an oligophrenic is given the problem: "In one pocket were two pens and in the other one more than this. How many pens were in the two pockets?", the mentally retarded child will make the conditions like some previously solved set when he reproduces them. He answers: "In one pocket there were two pens, in the other, one pen. How many pens were there in the two pockets?"

We have dwelt on these peculiarities of the intellectual functioning of child-oligophrenics, which emerge with extreme clarity in the process of mastering arithmetic and in problem-solving. However, it is possible to demonstrate with considerable success profound differences between the child-oligophrenic and his normal peer with instances of the peculiarities of the formation of his ideas, of his orientation in the surrounding world and in the characteristic features of the intellectual operations' which he can achieve.

It is well known that the child who is growing up in a family or is in a pre-school institution expands the scope of his ideas more and more as he grows. The information he obtains from the external world increases and becomes more complex.

With good reason some psychologists point out that the world of the infant is bounded by his field of vision and by the reach of his hands: the young child's world expands to the bounds of the room in which he lives, the street where he is taken for walks, and those relationships between adults with whom he comes into contact: information about the external world increases still further in the kindergarten and then in school. He knows his address and correctly appraises the relationships between members of the family: he quickly grasps the concepts of "brother", "sister", and "uncle." In play he finds out the connections and relations into which objects in the external world enter and his fund of information is further expanded. Speech with all its manifold connections and relations (and established as language) is added to his direct experience, and knowledge of an abstract character is added to his simple visual ideas about the world.

The normal child enters school possessing this knowledge, but the child-oligophrenic is in sharp contrast.

The disruption of the brain activity of such a child is manifested in the considerable constriction and impoverishment of the scope of the knowledge he has obtained of the external world and of the system of connections and relationships which he detects by the range of the ideas at his disposal.

It is possible to see with full clarity the constricted scope of the knowledge at his disposal during the first examination of a child with a severe form of oligophrenia.

Asked where he lives such a child (8 or 9 years old) frequently is limited to answering, "At home." Asked about his mother he can say nothing except that she is called "Aunt Katia". Asked about his father, he can only reply, "He works."

His knowledge of objects in the external world is just as narrow and impoverished. He can easily say that a dog has four legs, but after this he attributes four legs to a rooster and a duck; once the affirmation is made it is mechanically transferred to other objects. As I. M. Soloviev correctly observed: for the normal child the image of a pencil possesses a multitude of properties and can enter into a multitude of possible connections (the pencil can be small or large, sharp or blunt, round or many-sided, black, red, blue or green), but for the mentally retarded child information about the pencil is very restricted and he can barely name one or two distinctive details. It is by such attributes that other ideas of the child-oligophrenic are distinguished.

The poorness and inertness of these connections, into which the ideas of a mentally retarded child enter, result in a gross impoverishment of his perceptions and cognitions, of his understanding of simple material, and the intellectual operations at his disposal.

Psychologists are well acquainted with the development of the process of the perception of a thematic picture in the normal child. Many investigations have shown that the child who is given the task of examining and talking about a thematic picture only separates out discrete objects represented in the picture when he is an infant—subsequently he begins to denote their functions and properties. Towards the middle of the pre-school period he already gives a description of a whole plot represented in the picture in connected speech and he establishes connections and relationships between the separate objects depicted. By the beginning of school, the story about the thematic picture is very rich, and the young school child talking about a picture easily transcends the immediately perceptible content, discerns causes, conjures up various events, temporal connections between events and motives of the characters. He reveals the great richness and complexity of the processes of visual analysis and synthesis.

The perception of a thematic picture by a mentally retarded child is distinguished by quite different attributes.

A child with severe oligophrenia reveals the defects of his sense perception of the picture and of his speech analysis in particularly clear forms. For example, such a child who was talking about the content of the well known picture "Another Bad Mark!" was limited to saying: "There is ... a boy ... and a dog ... and a tail ... and an auntie ... and a girl." He did not even try to determine the actions of the characters or to combine them into a single common situation.

Defects of visual analysis and synthesis also emerge with sufficient clarity in less severe forms of oligophrenia. The child only establishes directly perceptible relationships between the individual details of a picture and he is unable to reflect the general idea correctly, particularly if it is necessary for him to transcend the bounds of direct perception and to include what is depicted into a general broad system of connections. These child-oligophrenics describe the picture "Another Bad Mark!" by saying, "There is a boy and the dog has jumped up at him ... and there is his mother sitting ... and there is a girl playing with dolls", but he does not grasp the original meaning of the picture. He describes the picture "The Widow" by saying, "There is an auntie ... she is wearing a black dress ... she is holding a handkerchief to her nose... she must have a cold." Of the picture "The Flood", which depicts a family saving itself from the flood by being on the roof of their country cottage, "There is a father, mother, and children... they are sitting... they must be having breakfast."

Frequently the experienced pedagogue can divine the deep disturbances in the intellectual functioning of the oligophrenic child from the fragmentation and poverty of his perception, from the inability to combine details into a single meaningful whole or to proceed beyond the limits of the immediately perceptible details in his treatment of the meaningful theme of the picture.

The poverty of the system of the meaningful connections characterizing the perceptions and ideas of the oligophrenic lead, however, to broader consequences. In part this determines the poverty of and limitations of the mental operations of the mentally retarded child.

At the end of the pre-school period and the beginning of school the child easily compares and contrasts separate objects and distinguishes their differences and similarities; he easily refers to these objects in the different situations in which they occur and in the first stages of school development he begins to generalize objects without difficulty and group them into their known categories. It was not without reason that K. D. Ushinskii viewed the generalization of objects on the basis of features which are first singled out, as one of the fundamental intellectual operations.

The mentally retarded child orientates himself quite differently.

Even a simple attempt to compare and contrast two objects or drawings reveals the total inadequacy of the operations which the mentally retarded child uses to solve the problem.

Most commonly the comparison of two objects and the discovery of what is common and what is not is just not used by such a child. He stubbornly begins to describe each object separately, announcing, "This is a butterfly. It is flying. It is in a garden. This is a fly. There are many in the kitchen. When meat is put down, many of them fly in."* Here where we expect the differentiation of certain basic features and the comparison of similar objects using these specially differentiated features we obtain a completely different activity from the mentally retarded child—a narration of well known, familiar, and consolidated reminiscences. He proves to be quite incapable of overcoming this. Even if we adopt the necessary measures and show him visually what we want to obtain from him, the child-oligophrenic is quite often incapable of executing the full operation of comparison. This operation will be slowly and sluggishly replaced by the production of two isolated systems of visual connections into which his perception of each object leads.

---

* I. M. Solovyev (Ed.), *The Peculiarities of Cognitive Functioning of Pupils in a Special School.* Moscow, Uchpedgiz, 1953.

The underdevelopment of the processes of abstraction and generalization and the insufficient participation of speech in the discrimination of the necessary features for the generalization of objects on the basis of the initially discriminated features, appear particularly clearly if we ask the child-oligophrenic to lay out a sample of pictures given to him, in groups—in other words, if we try to elucidate how his classificatory operations proceed.

This task does not present the ordinary school child with noticeable difficulty. He easily discriminates the relevant features in separate objects. Either he quickly hits upon the situation where all the selected objects occur together (for example he may say, "For a meal it is necessary to have a plate, tureen, knife, fork and spoon; in order to dress one needs a coat, hat, trousers and shoes"), or he notices a visual classification of a more abstract nature and discerns some feature present in the whole group of things or he refers the whole group of pictures to a general category "furniture", "crockery", "instruments", etc. A transference from one type of classification to another does not present him with special difficulty.

With the child-oligophrenic this process is quite different.

As a rule children with a severe form of oligophrenia are quite unable to achieve the requisite intellectual operations and they persistently continue to narrate what they know in connection with each separate picture and do not even begin to compare them. If the teacher, after prolonged explanation, constrains the child to begin such an activity, the defects of the child-oligophrenic become particularly apparent. Not infrequently he discriminates some completely immaterial, but visually obvious, feature and refers into one group a picture showing a wolf and one showing a garden bench—because they are both grey in colour. Such a comparison of things by directly perceptible, visual, yet immaterial, features (colour, form, size, the presence of some common particular details) not infrequently exhausts the processes of "generalization" in severe oligophrenics. For them the direct impression and not the special meaningful analysis plays the leading role in such "intellectual" operations. Sometimes it is similar with objects in spatial contiguity. They are directly included into a single common situation. The child unites, in one group, a plate, fork, knife and bread (because "It is necessary to cut it"), adds a chair and table ("It is necessary to lay the table, and it is necessary to sit on a chair"), and he continues this "classification" further and very quickly converts it into a reproduction of some visual and familiar situation, into which his perception of each object leads.

It is easy to see how much this basic symptom of the oligophre-nic—a profound disturbance in *the operations of abstraction and generalization*—dominates the whole of cognitive functioning.

This defect appears in other school operations of the child-oligophrenic and not only to a small degree. In all these it occurs with another symptom, which psychologists and pedagogues have frequently called "sluggish lability" of mental processes of the child and for the same reasons this can be designated *inertness*.

Many teachers in special schools complain that while it is difficult to get child-oligophrenics *to learn* something, it proves still harder for them *to unlearn* it. For instance, if a child-oligophrenic is given several arithmetical examples in addition and then he has to do one in subtraction, the child reads it out correctly but solves it in the same way as the preceding examples were solved. In the first class the teacher explains at the beginning of the lesson the concept of the number 10 and illustrates his explanation with tables on which fishes are painted (as a visual aid). After this, the following example is analysed and solved with the help of the teacher: "There were three birds sitting on a tree and two more arrived. How many birds in all were there on the tree?"

After this, when the problem has been solved, the teacher pro-posed that the children recall the problem by themselves. The major-ity of the pupils in the class were able to reproduce the conditions of the problem solved earlier exactly. Several pupils tried to alter somewhat the conditions of the problem given. For instance, pupil K. thought up the following example: "There were three fishes sitting on a tree and two more arrived. How many fishes in all were there on the tree?" This example shows the extreme inertia of connections once they are formed and this is quite characteristic of child-oligophrenics. This inertness often defines the peculiarities of the behaviour of these children. Thus when they have fully learned one school rule, they are unable without difficulty to change in association with a changed situation.

We have given a very cursory outline of those peculiarities in mental functioning which so sharply differentiate the child-oligophrenic from his normal peer. We have described two characteristic features of his mental functioning, the poverty and concreteness of the range of the knowledge at his disposal and the limitations and narrowness of the connections with which he operates. It is easy to see the extent to which both these features limit his capabilities in school activities and render the ordinary school programme inaccessible for him.

Now we need to consider a few further basic problems which their clinical study encounters.

3. *The Severity of Mental Retardation—Imbeciles and the Feeble-minded*

Teachers in special schools, and doctors, know that the degree of mental retardation in child-oligophrenics is far from being the same in every case.

Some children—usually termed *idiots*—are not only incapable of being taught, but are also unable to look after themselves. The under-development of their brains is so great that they usually need to be kept in institutions for chronic invalids. Others exhibit a similarly severe form of mental retardation; they can acquire elementary habits of looking after themselves, but they are unable to acquire the elements of grammar or arithmetic and only some of them can adapt themselves to the most elementary types of work.

With idiots it is not only the cerebral hemispheres which are damaged, but also the structure of other parts of the brain including the brain stem, the sub-cortical and diencephalic regions.

The severity and extent of the damage is revealed in the disturbances of physical development; in the malformation of the structure of the skull and skeleton; in the presence of endocrinal dysfunction and in general disharmony.

The motor behaviour of idiots is severely disrupted. Many exhibit disorganization in their standing and walking and not infrequently they are observed to make stereotyped movements in the form of a swaying of the trunk, a periodic clapping of the hands, shaking of the head and a sucking of the fingers. The normal fine movements of the hand are particularly disturbed in idiots. As a rule the majority of child-idiots are helpless; they have to be washed, dressed, have their hair done for them, to be fed and put to bed. Many of them are troublesome with their urinating and defaecating and require attention from the staff.

In severe forms of idiocy speech does not develop and with some idiots the development of speech does not proceed beyond the pronunciation of unconnected sounds. Cases have been observed where child-idiots can pronounce a limited number of words— but with distortion. Only in a few unique cases is the pronunciation aspect of speech better preserved, but even these children do not understand the sense or meaning of the words they do pronounce.

The behaviour of idiots is similarly sharply disturbed. Some of them are lifeless, apathetic, and almost never react to those around them. Many idiots are so lifeless that they do not react to bright and vivid stimuli. Others, on the other hand, are very easily spurred to activity and are restless. Both types, however, find it particularly difficult to fix their attention voluntarily.

The cortical functions of idiots are so disturbed that even the formation of simple conditioned reflexes is extremely difficult. Only some of them succeed in developing natural motor reactions. They acquire conditioned reflexes with great difficulty. In an attempt to produce differentiation any already established conditioned reflex is inhibited.

Child-imbeciles present a different picture. They suffer not only from damage to the cerebral hemispheres, but also from damage to the underlying regions (the spinal cord, sub-cortical-diencephalic areas, and nervous membranes).

Therefore, although imbecility is less severe than idiocy, the disturbance in physical development, manifested as a general dysplasticity and anomalous structure of the skull, is sufficiently apparent.

Less severe than with idiots, but still apparent in imbeciles, is the under-development of motor behaviour. Their motor behaviour is extremely undifferentiated and often they are unable to execute individual movements. Along with the general inhibition of these children one observes many superfluous movements of the hands and body. Particularly apparent in imbeciles are disturbances of fine, voluntary, movements. Because of this, imbeciles cannot look after themselves adequately and are unable to dress themselves or make their beds. Although the behaviour of imbeciles is less disturbed than that of idiots, the disruption of the complex forms of human behaviour is quite evident. Imbeciles are frequently unable to evaluate a situation and they behave inadequately.

When they are put into a school they do not understand that they have to study—that they must behave in a prescribed manner, and must do what the teacher tells them. During lessons they jump from their places, walk about the class, seize whatever comes to hand, break toys and tear text books and exercise books. The behaviour of imbeciles is under the influence of, and subject to, peculiarities in the emotional-volitional sphere. Some of them are listless, apathetic and inhibited, while others are uninhibited, excited and restless.

Child-imbeciles develop an attitude to the appraisals of the teacher and to their work only with difficulty. It is difficult to organize these uninhibited children into the process of education. They are poor at visually fixating a letter, number or picture presented to them. Teaching aids frequently serve only as objects for their manipulation.

Child-imbeciles are defective in their perceptual differentiation and their spatial notions are under-developed. They cannot distinguish between right and left. They cannot put together the most elementary figure out of sticks. The development of their speech functioning is disturbed. Most frequently the motor aspect of speech is as sharply under-developed as the sensory aspect.

The cognitive functioning of imbeciles is seriously under-developed and this leads to considerable difficulties in their learning of elementary grammar and arithmetic. They find it difficult to remember letters and frequently confuse letters which have some visual similarity or which designate similar vocal sounds. The deficiency of their auditory analysis and synthesis appears during their instruction in elementary grammar. Child-imbeciles master practical arithmetic with great difficulty and at first they correlate numbers and objects. The transition to abstract arithmetic usually proves to be beyond them. Frequently they only learn to iterate numbers and the multiplication tables mechanically.

Because of the under-development of their cognitive functioning, child-imbeciles do not discern the meaning of a simple thematic picture. They are able to enumerate the separate objects depicted in the picture, but they cannot discern and perceive their status or effects. For example, if an imbecile is shown a picture depicting a girl giving food to a hen, he recognizes the objects represented; but if he is asked, "What is the girl giving the hen?", then he will produce a stereotyped association, and will usually answer, "An egg." If he is shown another picture in which a cow is eating hay, then he finds it difficult to specify the depicted operation. If he is asked, "What is the cow eating?" then he may answer with an habitual stereotyped reply, "She is eating soup or porridge."

The inability of child-imbeciles to grasp the sense of an action in a picture results in the replacement of the intelligent answer by stereotyped associations from the personal experience of the child. The under-development of their capacity for abstraction and generalization appears particularly clearly in those types of activity in which the child-imbecile is required to abstract from concrete, and generalize from simple visual material. In this category is the simplified method of classifying objects, well-known under the title "the superfluous fourth one". In this, the child has to separate out from four objects (depicted on separate pictures) the one which clearly does not belong to the given category. The imbecile does not cope with this task, but selects all the pictures in turn. Characteristically, child-imbeciles make poor use of help accorded them.

For the majority of child-imbeciles more complex problems in the classification of objects or pictures are insuperable. The child-imbecile examines each picture in isolation, puts a name to it, but cannot unify them. After frequent repetitive instruction such a child either lays out all the pictures individually or he puts them in piles without regard to content.

It is not always easy for the doctor to diagnose the real degree of defect of a child. It is particularly difficult in those cases where a serious speech defect occurs against a background of general intellectual defect. Often these children are mistakenly referred to the category of the unteachable. However, proper, corrective-educational measures frequently make considerable progress possible in their development and can help them compensate for their defects to a certain extent. Consequently the so-called "special class" for seriously retarded children is inevitably the class in the special school for those with this diagnosis.

The unique form of oligophrenia known as "Mongolism"* is included in the imbecile category. This form is distinguished by characteristic peculiarities in both the physical and also the mental aspects of these children.

The cause of the occurrence of this illness has not been sufficiently explained. Anatomical examination of the brain shows a series of signs of under-development; the small size of the cerebral hemi-spheres, the poverty of convolutions. Microscopic examination discloses a delay in the development of nervous elements, as a result of which cells are observed which normally disappear in the sixth or seventh month of foetal life.

These children are similar to one another in their physical pecu-liarities. They have a unique type of face with almond-shaped eyes placed far apart. The eye sockets have raised outer corners, their noses are squat and their cheeks have a high colour. The mouth is half-open, the tongue is thick and creased with deep fissures; the teeth are small and irregular. The cranium is small in its meas-urements and the forehead sloped. The fingers of the hands are considerably fore-shortened and the joints are exceedingly pliant.

Diverse disorders in the ductless glands can be observed: the

* This is the English equivalent to the Russian, not a literal translation, which is Down's disease, after Langdon Down.

dryness of the skin, the dystrophy of the teeth, the fore-shortened stump-like feet and hands and a general reduction of the resistance of the organism.

Against the background of pronounced under-development of cognitive functioning in these children a series of specific peculiarities is particularly evident in their sensitivity to stimulation. While they are in the clinic these children imitate the gestures and actions of the doctor, teacher and nurse. Some of them are listless and passive, while others are, on the other hand, excitable, irritable and inclined to negativism.

From the two degrees of mental under-development described there can be distinguished in regard to degree of damage the feeble-minded who constitute the main body of children being trained in special schools.

There are reasons for believing that the cause of feeble-mindedness is a diffuse, and mainly superficial damage to the cerebral hemispheres, which results in the pathological factors described above. Such damage also means that we usually find that the feeble-minded deviate only slightly in their physical development and in many cases noticeable deviation in physical development is completely absent. In the majority of feeble-minded children clear defects in the motor system are revealed only in those instances when it is necessary to execute a movement according to a verbal instruction or in an imaginary situation. Thus for example, if a child has to imagine to himself a field with flowers in it and he has to act accordingly, i.e. pick flowers, then the feeble-minded child is incapable of doing so. However, motor disturbances in feeble-minded children are compensated for sufficiently, so that they do not prevent him from working eventually.

The feeble-minded are superior to imbeciles with regard to speech development and it is relatively rare to find that they have serious defects in the sensory or motor aspects of their speech.

Child-oligophrenics who are feeble-minded usually understand speech which is addressed to them. Only in the initial stages of instruction is there a prolonged period of physiological articulatory difficulty.

Disturbance of the motor and sensory aspects of speech in the feeble-minded is only observed in that form in which there is a combination of general intellectual deficiency and local damage to the auditory-speech system.

Under-development of the systematizing and generalizing function of speech is clearly apparent in the feeble-minded.

The basic peculiarities of feeble-minded children lie in the under-development of their cognitive functioning and this appears to only a less serious degree than in child-imbeciles. While the imbecile enumerates the separate objects coming into his visual field and does not detect the actions in the picture when he is describing a thematic picture, the feeble-minded child can understand the depicted action, but is unable to establish the system of connections necessary for the comprehension of the sense of the picture.

While the problem of classifying pictures is beyond the child-imbecile and he describes each picture independently, the feeble-minded child is able to combine pictures according to certain signs. The basis of these is the community of the concrete situation.

While imbeciles are able to master only the most elementary habits of grammar and arithmetic after prolonged instruction, the feeble-minded child can master the programme of the special school.

Feeble-minded children are also distinguished from child-imbeciles by the characteristics of their behaviour. They are much faster during the course of instruction in their beginning to understand the school situation and in their subordination to the teacher's demands. They are able to carry out individual tasks presented by verbal instructions. Many of them prove to have sufficient work-capacity to execute individual tasks within their scope.

Particularly sharp differences between imbeciles and feeble-minded children appear in the dynamics of their development. While only a very insignificant percentage of imbeciles are able to adapt to elementary types of work, feeble-minded children can, in the course of instruction, develop sufficiently to be able to attain a socially useful work-activity in the future.

4. *Basic Clinical Variants of Child-oligophrenics*

We have dwelt upon the characteristics of child-oligophrenics and have described children varying in the extent of their defects— characteristics which every doctor and teacher in a special school can observe.

However, such characterization is far from being adequate. Both the doctor and pedagogue-defectologist who are attentively studying such child-oligophrenics as imbeciles and feeble-minded children can easily see that individual children differ sharply one from another and that it is possible to divide both imbeciles and the feeble-minded into several groups which are characterized by profound individuality of behaviour and which require an appropriate approach from the pedagogue.

Some of these children are calm in their behaviour, easily subordinate themselves to the demands of the teacher, work with perseverance, and only reveal defects which are associated with the inadequacies of cognitive functioning which have been described above.

In other children the under-development of their cognitive processes is associated with serious defects in behaviour. Some children in this group are pathologically excitable, easily disinhibited, become restless, and are difficult to organize. Some, on the other hand, exhibit considerable proneness to exhaustion, are easily inhibited, and become listless and inert. The problems of the correct organization of their behaviour are as important for children of both groups as are the problems of teaching.

Some children are encountered among child-oligophrenics in whom a general under-development of cognitive functioning is combined with severe disturbances in the auditory-speech system, and, in others, with motor disorganization. In all these cases the special problem of directing them towards a compensation for the defects which they have arises—along with the general problems of training and education.

Finally, among child-oligophrenics, there are those children in whom the under-development of cognitive functioning is combined with a serious disturbance in spatial orientation and in motivation of behaviour. These children require special forms of corrective educational work.

Fundamental to the wide diversity in child-oligophrenics is the fact that the brain injuries leading to anomalous development can have dissimilar characteristics.

Diffuse, but relatively superficial cortical damage exists in all cases of oligophrenia (up to the severity of feeble-mindedness).

Just such a type of damage is observed in the first basic form of oligophrenia. Children with this type of damage to the central nervous system are usually calm and disciplined and reveal their defects in association with their deficiencies in cognitive functioning.

In other instances the cortical damage is combined with a surplus accumulation of cerebral fluid in the sub-arachnoid spaces and in the ventricles, that results in the functional activity of the cortex taking place under particularly pathological conditions. With the spreading of this process in the child-oligophrenic, the under-development of cognitive functioning is combined with serious defects in behaviour.

Finally, there are cases where the brain damage encompasses the superficial cortical layers differentially and where more serious damage occurs in individual systems.

Thus, when the predominant injury is to the auditory–speech area of the brain, a form of oligophrenia arises in which the under-development of cognitive functioning is combined with serious speech defects. In cases where the parieto-occipital sections of the brain are mainly affected, the oligophrenia is complicated by the appearance of agnosia and apraxia.

Finally, in those cases where the brain damage embraces the frontal system, the clinical picture presents not only an under-development of cognitive functioning but also a special disruption of motivation of behaviour and functioning.

The basic group of child-oligophrenics. Damage primarily to the cortex cerebral hemispheres is distinctive of that basic form of oligophrenia which is uncomplicated by additional factors.

The absence of gross changes of cortical neuro-dynamics in this form of oligophrenic is substantiated by the electro-encephalographic investigations, expounded in detail in a special chapter.

Clinical examination shows that the functioning of the individual sense organs in these children is not disturbed. Visual analysis and synthesis is preserved. They correctly recognize real objects put before them. They recognize pictorial representations of individual objects presented normally and as mirror images. They recognize geometrical figures and line drawings.

These children orientate themselves relatively well spatially. They have the concept of left and right. They copy correctly figures made out of sticks or matches and experience difficulty only when the tasks are substantially complicated.

Children in this group do not have pronounced disturbances in the sphere of motor behaviour. They have no kind of obvious disturbances in hearing. As a rule their speech is sufficiently clear and there may be no signs of articulatory difficulty.

An important characteristic of children in this group is the relative reservation of their behaviour. As a rule they are diligent, persevering, and organized pupils. In those cases when such a child has attended a crêche or kindergarten, there has been no mention of complaints about his behaviour. In school their behaviour remains correct. They subordinate themselves to the teacher's demands, attentively listen to the tasks given to them, and after a preliminary period of thought they give an answer. Emotionally these children are integrated. They are distressed by poor marks and pleased with good ones. They are to some extent capable of evaluating the work they have done and in this they display the elements of a critical attitude to their work. These children behave adequately in various situations. They are embarrassed in the company of adults, but behave more freely with children. To their elders they are polite and considerate. They have emotional ties with their relatives, the teacher, and their companions.

All these characteristics are combined in child-oligophrenics with deficiencies in cognitive functioning.

In their understanding of thematic pictures they find it difficult to establish a complex system of connections between the individual elements. They cannot achieve independent inferences from a narrative read to them when this contains a covert meaning or a missing link. The defective level of their development in generalization and abstraction appears with particular clarity in diverse forms of classification.

However, along with the insufficiently appropriate development in the emotional-conative sphere, the under-development of their cognitive functioning results in certain peculiarities in the behaviour of these children. Work-loving and persevering, they are frequently unable to find a way out of a situation incomprehensible to them. They understand all the teacher's directions literally, and in instances where the situation becomes more complex and it is necessary to change a decision in accordance with the changed conditions, singular difficulties arise for them.

For example, when such a child is on duty in the class, he strives to obtain absolute subordination to the established rules from the other children and if any child breaks the rules, the child on duty will fight him without regard to strength and ability. The conflict developed in these cases is only explained by the fact the child does not understand the situation.

When they are learning grammar these children are like other child-oligophrenics in that they experience notorious difficulties in the analysis of the vocal referent of each letter and in the combination of sounds into whole complexes. The good work-capacity of these children and their attentiveness to the tasks set them enables them to master the technique of reading. However, the transition from reading words to an understanding of the meaning of what is being read is retarded.

The difficulties in abstraction and generalization are revealed very clearly in the training of these children to do arithmetic.

Later on these children have great difficulties in solving arithmetical problems. They are frequently incapable of ascertaining the necessary meaningful connection between verbally expressed problems, numerical signs and designations.

To compensate for this it is necessary in the first place to util-

4

ize all those pedagogical methods which are directed towards the development of cognitive functioning.

In the execution of specific tasks it is essential to distract these children from old and inert connections, stimulate the formation of new connections, and teach them to make use of new impressions.

In instructing them in reading it is necessary continually to explain the meaning of the text being read to them, thus giving these children the opportunity of a better understanding of literary text to be read later on.

The organization of the behaviour of this variant of child-oligophrenic does not present special difficulties, however, and here it is necessary to take into account their specific characteristics.

We must remember that the child-oligophrenics of this group behave themselves adequately only in situations which they understand, and consequently it is necessary to explain, and explain thoroughly to them, in order to bring them to an understanding of the characteristics of a situation and it is necessary to teach them to vary their actions in accordance with a changed situation.

Excitable oligophrenics. There are those children who are distinguished from the group of child-oligophrenics just described because their general mental under-development is complicated by observed *defects in behaviour*. These are in some cases extremely excitable, uninhibited, and undisciplined children who have a sharply reduced work capacity. In other cases they are listless and extremely prone to inhibition.

What is the cause of these defects?

Careful clinical analysis shows that the combination of diffuse, but predominantly superficial, damage to the cerebral hemispheres and residual hydrocephalus (fluid in the brain) is critical for the evolution of this form of defect.

The presence of hydrocephalus in these children is substantiated by X-ray examinations which indicate changes in the configuration of the skull, thinning of the bones and "digital impressions" which have appeared as a result of an increase in the pressure inside the skull.

The disturbance in the circulation of the cerebral fluid and also in the normal circulation of the blood in child-oligophrenics of this group leads to the appearance of a series of symptoms. Bouts of head pains, sometimes accompanied by nausea and vomiting and having a clearly hypertensive character, vertigo, psychosensory disturbances and states of exhaustion which come on swiftly, must be considered as such symptoms. An examination of the nervous system shows that, as well as the slight, diffuse, and predominantly cortical symptomatology, there is a disturbance in the tonus of all muscle groups and slight disturbances in the co-ordination of movements and stature and in the liveliness of tendon reflexes. The neurological symptomatology is on the whole dynamic and variable.

The disturbances in behaviour which can be seen in children of this group are not all alike. Some manifest a predominance of the excitatory over the inhibitory processes and in others the inhibitory processes are dominant.

Children in whom excitatory processes are dominant are distinguished by a series of characteristic peculiarities even from a very early age. Already when they are of nursery age these children are not only retarded in their development, but are restless, irritable, capricious, and suffer from sleep disorders.

Along with the general disturbance in mental development a series of specific features are noticeable when these particular child-oligophrenics are of pre-school age: a general uninhibitedness and inability to concentrate, susceptibility to distraction and increased level of general excitability, and an inability to play with children.

When these children are of school age they begin to reveal disturbances in behaviour and a sharp decrement in work-capacity as well as an under-development of cognitive functioning. The uniqueness of children with this defect is clearly revealed in their motor system, in their behaviour and in their cognitive functioning. Their motor system is characterized not only by general signs of under-development, but also by the presence of super-fluous movements. Thus they rarely sit in class peacefully; they usually turn around, provoke their neighbours, aimlessly wave their arms about, move their feet and rummage about in their satchels. There is a tendency to accelerate the tempo of all move-ments. Hastiness, lack of inhibition, and disorder in the sequence of movements is characteristic of the motor system of these children.

They are distinguished by the peculiarities of their behaviour in that they are frequently excited, uninhibited, and susceptible to distraction—they react impulsively to everything going on around them. The behaviour of such children is highly depend-ent upon the circumstances in which they find themselves. In quiet circumstances with individual tasks they are more organized, but with changes in the situation they easily become excited.

Investigation of the limits of analysis and synthesis of indi-vidual analysers does not show up serious faults.

Visual perception is usually intact in these children; they re-cognize objects and their representations and drawn figures, but they give incorrect as well as correct answers. This is explained by the fact that they answer without thinking enough, not making the effort to examine the pictures well. Investigation of their spa-tial orientation also shows no gross disturbances, but again there are occasional impulsive answers as well as correct ones.

Children with this form of oligophrenia do not show special speech disturbances. They understand speech addressed to them sufficiently well, they build phrases properly, and they are good at repeating phrases which are difficult to pronounce. They cor-rectly differentiate correlated phonemes, thus showing the ade-quate preservation of the auditory perception of separate sounds. However, here also they often give impulsive as well as correct answers.

One of the outstanding characteristics of these children is their low work-capacity, an insufficiency of goal-directed activity. This peculiarity is manifested in their execution of any task. For ex-ample, poor fixation of tasks is shown in the building of pyramids and pictures out of cut up blocks. Such a child often launches into a task very quickly, without thinking about it and without preliminary analysis—and this is why he does not cope with it. These peculiarities are also revealed in an examination of their cognitive functioning. Thus in the experiment involving the classification of pictures, these children do not, as a rule, listen to all the instructions given them, and begin to manipulate the pictures, spreading them out in a disorderly way and incidentally uttering a series of collateral associations in connection with each individual picture. Frequently these incidental associations which come to mind lead them away from the resolution of the problems posed to them. However, when the behaviour of these children is organized by special methods, when they have to repeat back the instructions or the size of the task is reduced, they can succeed. This shows the defects in mental abstraction and generalization typical of oligophrenics. Hence, the characteristic feature on this group of oligophrenics is the ease with which they slide away from the tasks given into a series of collateral associations.

The bad work-capacity of this group of child-oligophrenics is clearly revealed in the course of their training in the conditions of a special school.

In the initial stage of instruction it is very difficult to attract the attention of such a child to a letter. He does not concentrate on the task and meanwhile produces a series of utterances irrelevant to the given task. For instance, if a series of letters with which the child is familiar is placed in front of him and he has to select out a given letter from the series, then he begins to rearrange all the letters, not making the selection of the letter named by the teacher. For these children the transition to syllabic reading is difficult. They frequently read through a word by guessing or by using the elements of a preceding word with similar letters. For these children writing is particularly difficult. They often write the elements of individual letters carelessly. Sometimes in the writing of a letter the children omit particular elements of it (for instance, "m" becomes the letter "n", "r" etc.)—or they write a superfluous element into a letter. Later on they misplace, forward, elements from the end of a word or a phrase, or they repeat an already written syllable, word, or phrase. The omission of vowels is frequently noted in these children. Such pupils approach written work very quickly, write carelessly and hurriedly, hand up their work first, and do not check it. The analysis of their work reveals inequality; there is a correctly written phrase and then there are mistakes in this very phrase when it is copied again. Omissions, unfinished pieces of writing, the merging of several words into one complex, misplacement of letters, words, and syllables—all these can be observed in both independent writing and in copying.

Particularly great difficulties appear during the instruction of these children in arithmetic. The enumeration of objects is very difficult for them because of their impulsiveness and the absence of fixation on the task. Thus, for instance, if a child is to take a specified number of "counting" sticks from ten such sticks laid before him, then in spite of the instruction given by the experimenter, he holds back and does not do the task. Should the child reach out towards the sticks, then all organized functioning disintegrates: the child clutches any number of sticks and sometimes grasps them all at once. If the child is asked to count off a certain number of sticks from a row of "counting" sticks spread before him, the child either counts off all the sticks or he stops, but not at the number which he was given. On the transition to addition and substraction with the first ten numerals the numerical estimations of this group of children are quite distinct from calculation and take on the character of an automatic enumeration of a series. In solving arithmetical problems the system of connections in the problems are not perceived by them and cannot prescribe their further action. In the process of solving problems they carry out fragmentary operations with numbers.

The dynamic investigations made on children with this form of the defect oligophrenia give us reason to consider that in these children—as well as the general under-development of the higher forms of generalization and abstraction common to all oligophrenics—there is a disruption of persistent goal-directed activity.

The inability of these children to persevere appears in all tasks and defines the peculiarities of their behaviour, since this is a fundamental obstacle in the way of successful training according to the programme of the special school.

Corrective-educational work with these children must be based on the qualitative uniqueness of the structure of their defect. To attain this end it is, in the first place, necessary to make use of all those pedagogical methods which are directed towards the organization of functioning. During such activities it is essential to abolish every type of stimulus irrelevant to the activity in hand. The impulsiveness of these children is clearly revealed in the course of their instruction. For the execution of complex activity the child must inhibit immediate reactions and must initially familiarize himself with the tasks given him. The inhibition of impulsive reactions must be the object of special teaching for children of this group. For the development of inhibited reactions it is necessary to make use of special exercises in rhythm, therapeutic gymnastics, and school tasks.

In the first stages of instruction the teacher organizing the behaviour and activity of such a child performs a certain task together with the child, since the latter cannot always organize his activity on the basis of the preliminary instructions of the teacher.

The profusion of collateral associations often lead children away from solving tasks given him. At first the childrens' activity has to be regulated by detailed verbal instructions from the teacher. Later on it is possible to incorporate the speech of the children themselves in planning their activity. The incorporation of their own speech in planning for these children has tremendous significance in the process of performing the task since it limits their garrulity, decreases the opportunity of sliding out of tasks and facilitates the organization of their activity.

As a result of a systematic application of special accessory means, it is possible to attain noteworthy improvements in the development of such children and enable them to become successful pupils in the special school.

Inhibited oligophrenics. Quite distinct from the children just described are those child-oligophrenics in whom inhibited reactions dominate their general behaviour and in whom fatigue appears so that they easily become listless, inhibited, and completely excluded from general work. These children retain the common feature of all oligophrenics: their capacity for abstraction and generalization is under-developed to the same extent as that of other retarded children. A proneness to inhibition and delay, listlessness as well as peculiarities of behaviour and of cognitive functioning are evident.

The origin of this defect usually lies in residual hydrocephalus in addition to diffuse cortical damage. Also in these cases X-ray examinations draw attention [to an abnormality in the size and form of the cranium, its vault and its base. In a series of cases in this group, poor and smooth relief of the internal laminae and thinning of the bones is noticeable and this indicates an overt form of hydrocephalus which has existed from early childhood. "Digital impressions" are apparent in all children in this group on the internal surfaces of the cranial bones around the cerebral hemispheres. This indicates later disruptions in the normal outflow of cerebro-spinal fluid. Disturbance in the effluence of fluid and in the cerebral blood circulation leads to the episodic occurrence of pains in the head, vertigo and, in individual cases, of psycho-sensory disorganization.

The characteristic features of the dominance of a state of inhibition in the cortex of these children is revealed in an examination of their higher nervous activity and in a study of the peculiar electrical activity of the cortex.

As with the groups of child-oligophrenics described above, no kind of separate disruptions of their hearing or vision or in their tactile or muscular sensitivity is noticeable in these children.

Such children correctly recognize pictures depicting individual objects, but their answers are usually extremely slow and often their reaction only occurs after the third or fourth presentation of a picture. When there is accumulation of general inhibition they either fail completely to name the presented pictures or they only name part of an object. However, additional stimulation immediately enables them to name correctly once more the pictures presented with the objects which they depict. An examination of their spatial orientation also reveals no serious disturbances, but in the execution of particular tasks they require additional stimulation or else their activity will periodically cease.

There are no serious defects on the motor side of these children. On stimulation they can perform individual motor tasks, but their movements are exceedingly slow, poor, and alike. When they are executing discrete operations with small objects it is possible to see that their pace gradually slows down, that their movements become weaker, decrease in amplitude, are gradually extinguished and disappear completely. There are no noticeable disturbances in auditory analysis, and their speech is normally adequately preserved. They understand speech addressed to them and can repeat correctly a phrase which it is difficult to pronounce. However, the precision of their pronunciation depends on their general condition. When there is an accumulation of inhibition their speech becomes slurred and incomprehensible. On re-activation the child begins to pronounce words clearly and precisely. On the whole speech is laconic, quiet, unexpressive, slow and indecisive.

However, all the disturbances described are not linked with persistent defects of any given analyser, but reveal the general neuro-dynamic peculiarities of this variant of defect.

The predominance of a state of inhibition appears clearly even at the very earliest stages in the development of these children. They do not react to sound or bright objects, and spend much time asleep in early childhood. Later on they are not interested by toys and do not play with other children. By pre-school age these children master walking and speech but still remain listless, passive, and do not manifest interest in playing and do not interact with those around them or with their relatives.

Towards school age they still remain listless and inhibited and are passively subordinate.

Against the background of an under-development of ability in abstraction and generalization, one of the peculiarities of cognitive functioning is an extremely slow perception of instructions for performing individual tasks. Additional stimulation is always necessary.

The development of their emotional life proceeds in an idiosyncratic way. Listlessness, passiveness, absence of reaction to the environment, reticence, and a tendency to negativistic reactions in the early stages of development give reason for mistakenly considering these children as children with an inert form of schizophrenia. However, the dynamic study of this group of child-oligophrenics shows that the degree of reduction of general inhibition is more clearly evident in the emotional-volitional sphere.

Already by the second year of school instruction the attitude of such a child to the evaluations of the teacher is clearly expressed. So is their reaction to poor appraisal and their emotional attachment to the teacher, relatives, and children. Later on with the reduction of general inhibition—the development of all aspects of personality increases more and more, and feelings of obligation and responsibility emerge in the execution of individual school tasks.

Prolonged clinical study of this group of children also reveals specific peculiarities in their behaviour. These children are characterized by listlessness, passivity, and susceptibility to inhibition. If they are not incited to activity and are not activitated, then they can remain indifferent and inactive for a considerable time. These children are constrained in situations to which they are not accustomed and their general inhibition becomes greater and negativistic reactions arise.

As we have already shown above, these children do not reveal pronounced disorganization in their movements, but their general susceptibility to inhibition leads to their motor system being unique. They move poorly and often lose their way. Mime is undifferentiated, poor, and rigid. Their gesticulations are cramped and indecisive. The tempo of their movements is slow and gradually

becomes slower and slower. Also fine movements are not sufficiently co-ordinated.

During their instruction in special schools their most obvious
difficulties are in learning to write. In their writing mistakes of
several types are noticeable—running together, perseveration, omissions of individual letters, syllables, and words. With appropriate help from the teachers, directed towards the activation of the
child, the quality of work improves and the number of mistakes
drops noticeably.

In solving arithmetical problems mistakes of various types
arise—perseveration, loss of individual elements—but when the
child is activated it improves.

The nature of the corrective-educational work in these cases
is defined by the quantitative uniqueness of the structure of this
defect. In work with these children all those methods which facilitate an increase in their activation must be used first of all. When
they are performing individual tasks it is essential to encourage
and stimulate them; sometimes the teacher himself needs to begin
to do the task along with the child. Sometimes it is useful for the
child to supplement his performance of the task with words.

In the course of the pedagogical work the teacher must appraise
correctly those nonsensical answers which these children give
when their inhibition grows. It must be remembered that unique
pseudo-negativistic reactions are distinctive of these children.
However, it is easy to lead them out of this state if one begins to
do the task along with the child. He quickly becomes involved
in the work and later on he will do the task by himself. Children
of this group are irksome, reticent, out of touch, easily lose themselves, become confused, are sensitive, are easily hurt and suffer
considerably as a result of their failures. It is essential to take all
this into consideration in the course of corrective-educational
training. It is necessary to help them to become involved in childrens' collectives, to give them commissions and to appraise their
achievements before the whole class.

Correctly organized pedagogical work stimulates the development of these children and enables them to do a job later on.

Oligophrenics with disturbances in hearing or in the auditory–speech system. Up until now we have analysed those groups of child-oligophrenics whose mental processes were equally under-developed and in whom no particular short-comings were noticed. However, among all the children in the special schools there are those who show obvious special defects against a background of general under-development. Sometimes among such children it is vision and the ability to orientate themselves spatially which suffers most, but sometimes disturbances in hearing and in the speech processes are particularly obvious.*

The characteristic feature of this form of oligophrenia is the combination of diffuse brain injury and more serious specific disturbances in the visual or auditory cortical areas.

We will now be concerned with that group of children in which specific disturbances in hearing and in the auditory–speech system is observed along with an under-development of complex forms of cognitive functioning.

The specific peculiarity in the pathogenesis of this form is the combination of diffuse damage to the cerebral hemispheres with more serious localized lesions in the auditory–speech zones of the left hemisphere. Neurological examination of this group shows a general under-development of the motor-system, lack of differentiation, awkwardness of movements and an abundance of superfluous accompanying movements as well as residual symptoms of a cortical nature.

Frequently these children exhibit apraxia of the lips and tongue and in connection with this the complex co-ordinated movements of the tongue, lips and larynx, i.e. the bases of speech articulation, are under-developed.

---

* This group of child-oligophrenics must be sharply delineated from those children mentioned in the last chapter, in whom disturbances in hearing are an isolated defect and do not occur against a background of general disruption of brain functioning. In that case it leads only to a secondary delay in development which is connected with the hearing deficiency. Such children are hard of hearing but completely normal. They are not given places in special schools and need to learn in schools for the deaf.

A study of operations which require visual analysis and synthesis does not reveal a serious pathology in these children. They correctly recognize objects and representations of objects presented to them. They recognize representations of individual pictures presented as mirror-images just as they also recognize geometrical figures. Similarly there are no noticeable and pronounced disturbances shown up by a study of their spatial orientation.

However, disturbances in hearing and all components of speech are manifested very clearly. Not being deaf (the auditory threshold of these children does not usually differ from the normal) these children most often cannot discriminate sounds similar in nature (for example, B and P, Z and S, D and T); they cannot separate out the separate sounds from continuous speech, nor can they repeat an unfamiliar word.

In the pronunciation of this or that sound they seek for correct articulation by means of series of fixed movements. Frequently the child opens its mouth with its fingers and checks the position of the tongue and lips. Their pronunciation of words is distorted. Distortions in their pronunciation of individual phrases are manifested with particular clarity.

Their ability to differentiate complicated sound complexes is under-developed. They find it difficult to abstract an individual sound from a whole word and conversely they find it difficult to gather a word into the appropriate sound complex.

Naturally, sound-letter analysis is also difficult for them to attain. The writing of even simple words is extremely difficult for them.

Frequently these children display an insufficiently precise understanding of speech addressed to them.

The disturbance of all components of speech is manifested by child-oligophrenics of this group against a background of general under-development of cognitive functioning. Thus in the experiment involving picture classification they are only capable of combining identical pictures; they cannot lay out pictures in a certain sequence. Their deficiency in cognitive functioning is exhibited in their difficulty in mastering arithmetic and like other child-oligophrenics, they find it particularly difficult to grasp the sense of arithmetical problems.

The behaviour of these children does not present great difficulties and under the organizing influence of the teacher they become adapted to school life. They willingly execute individual errands, show interest in school activities and carefully perform those tasks that they can manage.

All the pedagogical work with the children of this group needs to be built around the qualitative uniqueness of the structure of the defect.

In the very early stages it is necessary to provide a series of special activities for the correction of their motor system, simultaneously providing speech training activities. In the course of school instruction the teacher operates on the positive aspects of the child's personality and on the better preserved analysers and in everything he needs to stimulate the development of speech. In these cases it is particularly necessary to conduct systematic work with the parents and give them concrete instructions concerning the development of the motor system and speech.

Oligophrenics with gross under-development of personality. Sharply different from the described forms of oligophrenia is that where a gross under-development of personality appears clearly against a background of under-development in cognitive functioning. The systems of needs and motives are deviant. This basic defect is, as a rule, accompanied by unique under-development of the motor system.

In the peculiarities of their behaviour these children are reminiscent of adults who are ill as a result of damage to the frontal areas of the cerebral hemispheres. (Many authors have associated these areas with the higher and most complex forms of active behaviour.)

These children are not encountered very frequently among the whole mass of child-oligophrenics. However, both doctors and pedagogic-defectologists have to discriminate the children of this group in order to appraise them correctly and to find a useful approach to them.

They are distinguished from all other child-oligophrenics by the sharply pronounced individuality of their behaviour.

These children have no pronounced attitude to the people around them—to their parents, teacher or to children. They are incapable of interacting with children and adults. Their behaviour does not change when they find themselves in a new situation which is unfamiliar to them. Thus, for example, in the doctor's office where they go first of all, they take hold of and sort out objects lying on the table, throw them, chatter continuously, go up to adult strangers, tug them by their dresses or ties, pose an innumerable quantity of questions and do not listen to the answers. These children have none of the elementary forms of shyness; feelings of awkwardness are unfamiliar to them. The majority of them are incapable of feeling hurt. Their behaviour has no persistent motives. They often refuse to do a set task for no reason. It is sufficient to satisfy some desire of such a child to persuade oneself that this desire was not the underlying nor real aspiration. Once he has obtained a toy he has demanded, he sometimes does not even look at it but, puts it on one side or throws it on the floor and asks for another one. The same happens with pictures and games.

All these features are associated with a serious under-development of the brain, in this case with an uneven diffuse character but predominantly expressed in the under-development of the frontal lobes. A neurological examination of these children reveals, quite clearly, serious disturbances in the motor system against a background of symptoms of lesions over the whole cortex.

Motor disturbances can be expressed in varying degrees. In the most serious cases every movement which instructions require to be performed evokes a general motor storm. Thus, for example, if a child has to fasten a button, then he first makes sweeping imprecise movements with his hands, movements of the torso and only gradually do the hands approach the button. He makes several contacting movements, finds the buttonhole, tenaciously grasps and holds it. With his free hand he makes approximately as many movements around the button and then, but not immediately, he clutches it with several grasping movements. Only after several such movements can he finally fasten the button.

Whilst there is no paralysis and paresis, every movement which these children are instructed to make evokes considerable difficulties for them.

Even in less serious cases in similar children, the same motor disturbances are clearly manifested. Such children are awkward and clumsy in their movements, cannot look after themselves and many of them develop poor motor skills. Some exhibit a deviant posture and it is possible to speak of apraxia in walking, i.e. an inability to control the legs usefully, and all this can appear in the absence of paresis. A study of motor behaviour shows that such children execute even simple movements very uncertainly with searching motions and sometimes in reversed directions. Synthesizing trials requiring the simultaneous participation of both hands are particularly difficult for them.

All their movements are only feebly automatic. Once aroused movements have become sluggish, they can be re-activated only with difficulty. The most characteristic peculiarity of their motor system is the ever present discrepancy between the movements which they perform themselves and those movements which they have to perform on the orders of the teacher.

They show a complete inability to make a particular movement when ordered to, but they can make this movement spontaneously without any difficulty. It is possible to suggest that the disturbance in the frontal regions of the cortex (which are anterior to the motor area and dorsal to the sub-cortical motor ganglia) leads to a disruption of the organization of movements at a higher functional level.

It is by these disturbances in the higher aspects of the motor system that the symptoms observed in child-oligophrenics of this group are explained.

In this group we are describing there is a unique form of under-development in speech, which sharply differentiates it from all other forms of oligophrenia.

These children have no disturbances in pronunciation. They

begin to speak almost at the same time as normal children and they pronounce correctly words and phrases which are difficult to say. Their tendency to imitate the speech of adults also substantiates the idea of the absence of serious disturbances. They have no disturbances on the sensory side of speech either. They understand speech addressed to them and do not experience particular difficulties in the mastering of sound-letter analysis.

However, the role which the speech function plays in the differentiation of the motives for activity, in the building-up of intelligent action, and the development of willed behaviour, is particularly disturbed.

The child of 4 or 5 accompanies his activities with utterances containing statements of the difficulties which have arisen for him. Gradually this external speech is transformed into internal speech which plays a special role in the development of complex forms of human behaviour.

It is just this regulatory function of speech which is especially seriously disturbed in the child-oligophrenics of this group. They are unable to subordinate their actions to verbal instruction. Even if they retain and repeat back the instructions given to them, they are still unable to subordinate their actions to these instructions. Frequently these children accompany their activity with verbal utterances which have, however, no relation to the task they are performing and which are irrelevant. For example, a boy is given the task of building a picture out of cubes. He accepts the task and he twirls the cubes around saying. "It is warm, it is warm on the street, spring days", and then inserts from the speech of the adults surrounding him, "Please, be so kind, thank you."

If the generalizing function of speech is fundamental meditative activity, then naturally the regulatory function of speech is associated with the formation of the emotional-volitional sphere of personality.

Therefore, with child-oligophrenics of this group, the emotional-volitional sphere of personality is under-developed as well as the regulatory function of speech.

In child-oligophrenics of this type there are severe disturbances

5

in their capacity for goal-directed activity. While a child of 3 or 4 hears an instruction given to him, and then executes his intention, child-oligophrenics do not attain this level and often substitute a meaningless manipulation of objects for the performance of the task given them.

Goal-directed activity, i.e. activity defined by motives, requirements and elementary emotional interests, is considerably disturbed in all these children. For example, such a child often begins to read a book handed to him and he reads everything printed on the cover from above, sideways, from below, the year of publication etc. If he is interrupted and again given the book he will go through the same procedure. He will even do it a third time. Often this same child reads the text in reversed order which makes what is read completely nonsensical.

The characteristic feature of children in this group is the peculiarities] in behaviour and these distinguish them from all the groups described earlier. Some of them are listless, passive, and wholly subordinate. These children easily subordinate their behaviour to the established rules but they are not able to comprehend these rules fully. Other children are very excited. Feelings of fear, constraint and embarrassment are foreign to them. These children have no persistent relationship to a situation or persons around them.

Frequently active forms of behaviour are substituted for by their inclination to imitation.

Unique peculiarities characterize the overt features of their emotional life. These children show immediate affective reactions and are therefore lively in interviews with their relatives. Along with this, however, is an absence of deferred affective reactions and there is no generalized emotional relationship.

Investigations of their cognitive functioning show that difficulties in the solution of a conceptual problem arise not only because of difficulties in perceiving the abstract significance of words or inability to grasp complex abstract relations, but also because of serious disturbances in their goal-directed activity. When they are solving intellectual problems these children easily lose sight of the real motive for doing so. Their actions begin to be subordinated to incidental impressions and produce automatic pointless tendencies.

Corrective-educational work with children of this group has to be based on the qualitative uniqueness of the structure of the defect.

In the first place all those pedagogical methods are utilized which are directed towards the organization of their motor system and activities with objects. The development of their motor system must be carried out in special activities and in the course of their activities with objects. Along with this it is essential to train them in their relationships with and interest in those around them from the very earliest age.

The training in interest is realized most effectively in the course of play activity. Only later is it possible to transfer to the organization of their activity with objects.

We must remember that the under-development of the regulatory function of speech is the basic obstacle preventing the development of goal-directed activity of these children. Therefore, initially the regulation of the child's activity needs to be realized by the speech of the teacher and only subsequently ought there to be a transition to the stage when the children learn to regulate each individual element of activity by their own speech. This stage must be continued until the child learns to perform a task without talking aloud before he performs it.

The organization of the behaviour of these children is the most difficult section of the corrective-educational work.

At first the pedagogue must verbally appraise those impressions, which the child perceives to produce a method of action. The child under the control of the teacher realizes a worked-out mode of action. Then the child, with the help of the pedagogue, appraises the impressions received, formulates them in speech, chooses modes of action concordant with the appraisal of the impressions and also makes a preliminary formulation of the mode of action in speech. This protracted stage of the work leads to a certain compensation for the condition of such children.

5*

5. *Other Forms of Mental Retardation in Children*

Children with mental retardation following meningo-encephalitis. There are children studying in special schools who have suffered from encephalitis and meningo-encephalitis with varying aetiology in early childhood.

Residual manifestations of para-infectious encephalitis are extremely diverse. Most frequently in the residual stage of para-infectious encephalitis there are noticeable changes of intellect and disorganization of behaviour and character. Children like this are sensitive to stimulation, are excited above average, irascible, disinhibited, and their moods are unstable.

In certain cases there is a tendency to affective outbursts and increased appetites.

The structure of the defect in the post-encephalitic conditions is distinguished by a certain singularity. In some cases pronounced disturbances of complex forms of mental functioning are combined with diverse local disturbances appearing as paralysis, paresis, speech defects, optical defects and defects of optical and spatial analysis and synthesis.

In other cases, a combination of disturbances of the higher forms of cognitive functioning with changes in the emotional–volitional sphere is more evident.

These states need to be delimited: on the one side from oligophrenia and on the other from childhood psychopathological states. These states are distinguished from oligophrenia by the fact that in oligophrenia the disruption in development begins in utero or in the very early stages of the child's life. In residual post-encephalitic states, anomalies of development arise at different stages of growth and are associated with the infection experienced.

In the residual stages of para-infectious encephalitis we frequently notice a combination of substantial disturbances in cognitive functioning and changes in the emotional–volitional sphere. A similar combination of symptoms is rarely encountered in oligophrenia.

More serious defects in a particular analyser in combination with a disturbance in cognitive functioning are more frequently encountered in the residual stage of para-infectious encephalitis.

Mentally retarded children with active epileptic processes. These are children in the special schools whose mental retardation is explained by current epileptic processes.

Epilepsy is related to those neuro-mental illnesses which most often begin in childhood or adolescence.

Substantial anatomical changes in the central nervous system take place when epileptic processes are present: scars, shrunken cells, swollen fibres in cells, excessive growth of cellular tissue, changes in the ventricles of the brain, an accumulation of fluid in the sub-arachnoid spaces, and atrophy of the cortex.

Epileptic fits are one of the basic characteristic signs of epilepsy. The epileptic fit divides into four phases. The first stage can be very variable in its manifestation. Frequently unpleasant sensations in various parts of the body and imprecise sensations of light precede the beginning of a fit. In other cases the initial phase is manifested in motor behaviour—the child has a strong desire to run somewhere, turns round and round on one spot, and cries out individual words.

Visual or auditory hallucinations can precede a fit. The second phase is expressed as a loss of consciousness and a loss of tonus in the musculature. The child falls. In the third phase, subsequent to the initial relaxation there is a general tension of the musculature with a pronounced increase in the strength and rate of the pulse. Tonic convulsions are usually associated with clonic ones. These are expressed in the abrupt flexion and extension of the body's extremities, twitching in the facial muscles and spasmodic jaw movements which are the cause of biting the tongue. During the fit affected children frequently utter inarticulate sounds and gurgle; this depends on the spasmodic contraction of respiratory muscles and the muscles around the larynx. During the fit the pupils of the eye are dilated and do not respond to light. Frequently there is involuntary urination and defaecation.

The fourth phase—the end of the fit—is characterized by a relaxation of the musculature and either a more or less fast restoration of consciousness.

Apart from the described fits various types of change in pattern

can be observed. In "petit mal" there is only a briefloss of consciousness with no convulsions: consciousness is lost only momentarily,
then the children quickly come to and continue whatever activity
they had begun. Frequently typical fits can be observed which
manifest themselves in motor disorganization; children begin to
turn round and round on one spot and suddenly rush forward.
In some cases an atypical fit is characterized by expressive movements
(laughter, crying).

Apart from the convulsive fits in children suffering from epilepsy
there are various types of mental change. These children frequently
exhibit periodically occurring changes of mood which are characterized by their becoming capricious, irritable, insolent, captious,
morose, and dissatisfied with those around them.

As well as having mood changes these children sleep-walk and
have nocturnal fears.

Changes in cognitive functioning are extremely characteristic
of certain forms of epilepsy. The disturbances in cognitive functioning unique to epileptics is the slowing-down of the rate of all
mental processes.

Such children perform any task very slowly. They move, eat,
and dress slowly, and they read, write, and do arithmetic even more
slowly. The slowness of their speech is manifested not only in its
tempo. These children have difficulty in selecting required words,
and they introduce into their speech a series of additional words
like "well" and "it is" persistently and repeatedly.

Disturbances in the capacity to abstract and generalize are particularly evident in epileptics. In solving problems involving the
classification of pictures they not only do not utilize help given to
them, but confidently answer that such objects, for example, a cup,
a spoon, a saucepan, and a fork cannot be united under one word,
since tea is drunk out of a cup, soup is eaten with a spoon, soup
cooks in a saucepan, while meat is eaten with a fork.

The extremely sluggish lability of mental processes is a particularly characteristic and specific peculiarity of epileptic feeble-
mindedness.

The epileptic who has got stuck in the performance of some aspect of an activity cannot switch to another aspect.

Epileptic children often perform the tasks they are given very carefully and accurately because of the significantly greater slowness of their mental processes. The reduction in cognitive activity in epileptic children is combined with changes in character. They are frequently irritable, greedy, rude, ugly, and pretend to be nice. Epileptics suffer from a particular state of affective tension that is frequently expressed in their proneness to sharp affective discharges.

All the specific peculiarities of epileptic feeble-mindedness are associated with the current pathological process, which leads to a change in higher nervous functioning.

The clearly pronounced disturbance in the lability of the basic nervous processes is the most characteristic peculiarity of their higher nervous activity.

Epileptic children who suffer from infrequent or nocturnal epileptic fits and epileptic feeble-mindedness need to be directed for training in special schools.

Under the conditions of a special school epileptic children require individual methods of approach.

In working with these children the teacher needs to operate on the positive aspect of a child's personality. Examples of the work of these children, which are frequently very good in the carefulness of their execution, are useful for demonstration in front of the other children and such examples can be appraised in the appropriate way. The pedagogue can usefully allow for the slowness of the responses of epileptic children by giving them their tasks first and examining their tasks last in the class. This last method increases the time for the epileptic child to complete his work (and it is necessary). It gives him the chance of finishing the task along with the other pupils in the class. At the same time the pedagogue must take into account the possibility of periodic deterioration in the child's condition and during that period he should lessen his demands on the child and protect him.

The conjunction of a correct individual method of approach and treatment creates an opportunity for the advancement of such children under the conditions of the special school and an opportunity for their later adaptation to some useful form of work.

Children with mental retardation following late traumatic brain damage. Among the pupils in special schools are these children whose mental retardation developed as a consequence of a brain trauma received in childhood.

The symptoms of traumatic brain injury are extremely varied and depend on many factors, the nature of the traumatic damage, the age at which the damage was sustained, the amount of brain affected by the injury, the particular state of the child just before a traumatic illness.

In the final stage of concussion of the brain, headaches, dizziness, increased susceptibility to exhaustion, and reduced work-capacity occur most often.

The combination of reduced work-capacity with a disturbance in cognitive functions gives justification to a diagnosis of traumatic feeble-mindedness and justifies sending the child to the special school.

Frequently the structure of a traumatic defect is complicated by the fact that a disruption of the functioning of a particular analyser is combined with a disturbance in cognitive functioning and reduced work-capacity resulting from a local haemorrhage evoked by the brain trauma.

*   *

*

We have examined the separate groups of child-oligophrenics and those groups of children who ought to be distinguished from them. All child-oligophrenics are distinguished by one common feature: a serious disturbance in the development of the brain has resulted in the under-development of complex forms of cognitive functioning; it has led to limitations and paucity in the information which these children can receive from the external world; and to an inertness and a lack of lability in the basic aspects of their activity. However, as well as this we have been able to describe many other features which discriminate children in this group. We have pointed out the diverse degrees of excitation and inhibition of these children. We have pointed out that clearly pronounced specific and particular defects are noticeable in some of them, against a background of general under-development.

What lies at the root of these forms of under-development in brain functioning? Which mechanisms of higher nervous activity destroyed by pathological conditions lead to such a pathologically changed form in their mental processes?

In subsequent chapters of this book we will try to answer these questions now that we have thrown some light in individual chapters on the peculiarities in the functions of their brains and the peculiarities of those higher nervous processes which distinguish them from their normal peers.

CHAPTER 3

PECULIARITIES OF THE ELECTRICAL ACTIVITY OF THE BRAIN IN CHILD-OLIGOPHRENICS

WE HAVE considered the data obtained in clinical, psychopathological, and neurological investigations of child-oligophrenics. However, our information is not limited to data concerning their behaviour and mental peculiarities.

New opportunities of studying the functional characteristics of the nervous system have emerged among the methods facilitating the investigation of the nervous system, in combination with the widely used clinical and psychological investigations. These opportunities have arisen in recent years through the development of an area of physiology—electro-physiology.

Electro-physiological methods of investigation provide one of the most sensitive indices of the activity of tissues because even the most insignificant changes in organs and tissues lead to changes of electrical potentials. Thus electrical potentials arise in the skin at the very lightest touch and in the working muscles of the eye when it contracts insignificantly or when it is illuminated.

It is known that nervous tissue occupies a special place among the tissues of the body. The nervous system directs all the functions of the organism and is therefore in a state of continuous activity. This is explained by the fact that in contrast to all other body tissues, the nervous tissue constantly exhibits changes in electrical activity.

In 1892 the founder of Russian physiology, I. M. Sechenov, discovered the existence of uninterrupted oscillations of electrical current in the brain of the frog. In 1912 Pravdich-Neminskii discovered periodic oscillations of electrical potentials in the dog's brain and finally in 1923 the Belgian scholar, Berger, obtained a record of currents from the human brain. At first Berger used needles attached to the scalp in order to obtain his records of electrical potentials. This method was quickly replaced by the simple attachment of metal discs to the scalp, since these also conducted the electrical potentials which arise in the cortex. The metal discs were connected to special recording instruments. This means of leading off the electrical potentials of the brain was simple and quite harmless and therefore quickly passed into physiological and medical practice as a method for investigating human beings.

Since the electrical potentials of the brain change with the various changes in the state of the organism, the investigation of them is usually conducted under conditions of isolation and reduced illumination so that irrelevant stimuli have no effect. The person being examined sits in a comfortable armchair or reclines on a divan. Everything is directed towards the creation of conditions of maximal quiescence during the recording of the electrical potentials.

Special investigations established that the electrical activity of the brain of a relaxed man is characterized by rhythmic oscillations of a specific frequency. The most typical rhythm in man is between 8 and 13 cycles per second—the alpha-rhythm as it is called—and this is distinguished not only by its specific frequency but also by its spindle-shaped form (Fig. 1). In the majority of healthy adults the alpha-rhythm prevails over all regions of the brain and is particularly evident in the occipital parts.

As well as the alpha-rhythm there are other rhythmic electrical potentials, for example the beta-rhythm with a frequency of 18–25 cycles per second. Frequently certain rhythms are superimposed on others yielding a rather complex record consisting of a series of oscillations of differing frequencies—the so-called electro-encephalogram.

Each person has a unique type of cerebral electrical activity. If we take currents from several people twice, the second after a relatively short time interval, then it can be seen that each person retains his unique type of electrical activity.

Along with the existence of these individual differences and variations, the electrical activity of healthy persons of a given age has certain general features. This has decisive significance, since the existence of a set pattern of electrical activity for healthy persons enables any change in this to be used to assess any disease which has developed.

Studies have shown that the electrical activity of the brain of oligophrenics is different from that of normal children of the same age.

The cerebral electrical activity of the normal child recorded under conditions of complete relaxation is characterized by a rhythm whose frequency is about 10 cycles per second (alpha-rhythm). The alpha-rhythm prevails as a rule over the whole area of the two cerebral hemispheres in normal children over 13 years old. A record of the cerebral electrical potentials of a normal child is shown in Fig. 1.

The character of the cerebral electrical activity of the mentally retarded child is substantially different. The alpha-rhythm is absent and in its place are registered curves of slow oscillations with a frequency of 3–4 cycles per second—the so-called delta-waves. Delta-waves are characterized by their large amplitude and unique configuration. They are characteristic of severe impairment of cortical functions and are usually encountered when there are gross organic brain lesions (Figs. 2, 4, 5).

The established differences between the cerebral electrical activity of normal children and oligophrenics permits the utilization of the electro-physiological method of studying the extent and character of brain lesions due in this affection.

A comparison of electro-encephalogram data with the clinical profiles of oligophrenics showed that in the overwhelming majority of cases the severity of the oligophrenia corresponded to the extent of the disturbance of the cerebral electrical activity. The correspondence between the severity of defect in and the extent of disturbance of cerebral electrical activity within oligophrenics is clearly exposed when two groups of oligophrenics—imbeciles and the feeble-minded— are compared. The electro-encephalogram of imbeciles is particularly characterized by the poor expression of the alpha-rhythm

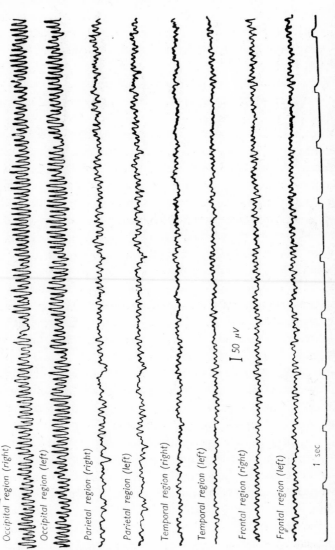

FIG. 1. A record of the electrical potentials of a girl pupil (13 years old) in an ordinary school. The alpha-rhythm with a frequency of 11 c/s is dominant in all cortical areas.

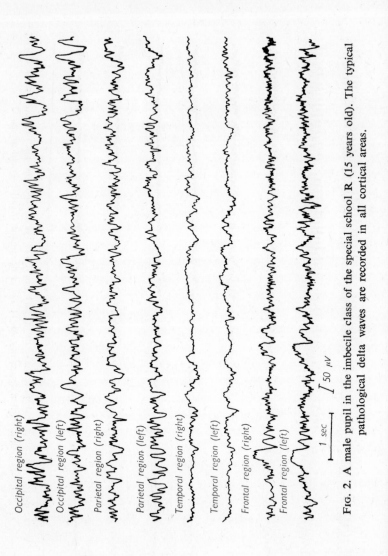

Occipital region (right)

Occipital region (left)

Parietal region (right)

Parietal region (left)

Temporal region (right)

Temporal region (left)

Frontal region (right)

Frontal region (left)

1 sec

50 μV

FIG. 2. A male pupil in the imbecile class of the special school R (15 years old). The typical pathological delta waves are recorded in all cortical areas.

and the existence of slow pathological waves frequently looking like delta-waves. The electro-encephalogram of a student from imbecile class R (15 years old) can serve as an example. When a child at the breast he suffered from meningo-encephalitis. From his early years his development was severely retarded. A neurological examination disclosed a severe bilateral symptomatology chiefly on the right, and pronounced sub-cortical lesions. An investigation of his psychological condition showed a severe behaviour disturbance, a complete absence of grasp of the situation. His intellect was sharply depressed: the child could not execute the most elementary tasks (he had no concept of number, could not cope with elementary reading, his speech was very retarded with an echolalistic repetition of a given question).

In Fig. 2 it can be seen that the slow pathological delta-waves prevailed over all cortical regions.

The correspondence between the electro-encephalogram and the severity of defect can also be seen in the less severe type of oligophrenia—feeblemindedness.

A girl pupil from the sixth form of an auxiliary school C can serve as an example. The aetiology of her illness was unclear. Speech disorders were the main feature of the clinical profile. No overt neurological symptomatology was present. Her behaviour was normal. There was some under-development in her abstract forms of thinking. Difficulties in education were explained mainly by the existence of the speech defect. In terms of her mastery over her speech defect she began to improve well under the programme of an auxiliary school.

The recordings in Fig. 3 show that in this case the electro-encephalogram departed only slightly from the norm. A fairly sharply defined alpha-rhythm was registered in all cortical areas although it was possible to pick out some irregularity in the occipital regions and there were slower oscillations mixed with the alpha-rhythm in the forward areas.

In contrast to this the records of Fig. 4 are those of an oligophrenic with a considerably more serious clinical profile—a pupil from the 6th class from auxiliary school F. He had suffered from a disturb-

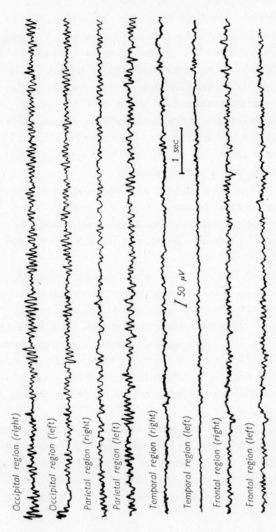

Occipital region (right)

Occipital region (left)

Parietal region (right)

Parietal region (left)

Temporal region (right)

Temporal region (left)

Frontal region (right)

Frontal region (left)

1 sec

I 50 µV

FIG. 3. A female pupil V in the 6th class of a special school (13 years old). There is a slight degree of oligophrenia with a predominance of speech disorganization. Pronounced deviations from the normal are absent from the EEG. In the occipital areas the alpha-rhythm is uneven. In the parietal (central) regions the alpha-rhythm is mixed with slow waves.

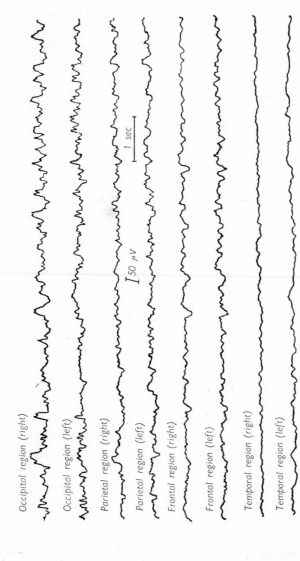

Fig. 4. The EEG of a male pupil in the 6th class of the special school P (13 years old). Severe oligophrenia. A pronounced deviation from the normal in the electrical activity of the brain. Slow waves are recorded in all regions of the cortex.

ance of intra-uterine development, complicated by an infection with meningeal characteristics at 4 months. The retarded development began in the first years of life and was particularly apparent in the pre-school years.

A neurological examination revealed a diffuse neurological symptomatology. Psychologically there was a considerable inefficiency of cognitive activity. Working ability was noticed to be inferior, there was an abnormal susceptibility to exhaustion and the boy frequently slid out of the tasks given him. He found difficulty with the programme in the auxiliary school. In accordance with this severity of the oligophrenia, the electro-encephalogram showed pronounced departure from the normal cerebral electrical activity. Slow pathological waves were registered in all cortical regions. Typical delta-waves appeared periodically in all cortical areas.

The comparison of the electro-encephalogram and the clinical profile of oligophrenia show that *the character of the changes in electrical activity of the brain reflect the qualitative uniqueness as well as the degree of defect.*

As we have pointed out above (see Chapter 2), it is possible to discriminate variants of defect among child-oligophrenics. The form of oligophrenia with pronounced neurophysiological disturbance is most important. In these cases, as well as the underdevelopment of the complex forms of mental activity common to all oligopherenics, additional symptoms can be observed, which indicate a gross disturbance of the balance of the excitatory and inhibitory processes.

The analysis of material obtained from a study of the electrical activity of the brain shows that when oligophrenia is not complicated by gross neurophysiological disturbances, cerebral electrical activity usually deviates less sharply from the normal. Conversely where oligophrenia is complicated by a gross disturbance in the balance of the excitatory and inhibitatory processes, the electroencephalogram frequently shows considerable departure from the norm.

As an example we can site the wave record in Fig. 5, obtained from a pupil (9 years old) in the second class of the special school K. Her clinical profile is one of clear neurophysiological disturbance.

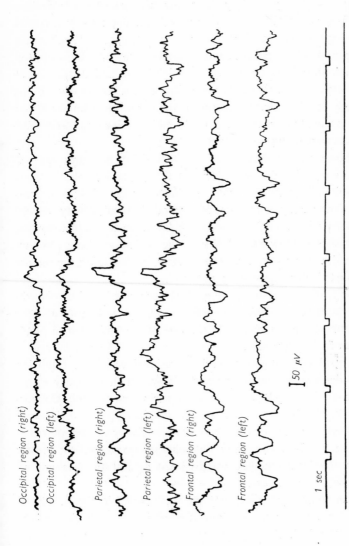

Fig. 5. The EEG of a pupil in the 2nd class of special school K (9 years old), with a diagnosis of "oligophrenia–imbecility", complicated by gross neuro-dynamic disturbances. The slow pathological waves predominate on the EEG.

The medical record shows an intra-uterine trauma. From an early age she was distinguished by superfluous ability and motor restlessness. A neurological examination revealed a slight bilateral symptomatology of a transient nature. Psychologically, against the background of a general under-development of the cognitive processes there was proneness to disinhibition and distraction.

During school activities she exhibited abrupt fatigue when doing academic tasks. Towards the end of the period the number of her mistakes usually increased, and she would give incorrect and ridiculous answers along with correct ones.

Following the utilization of special training measures she was able to cope with the programme of the special school.

In spite of the absence from the clinical profile of signs of gross injury to any analysers, studies of cerebral electrical activity showed pronounced deviation from the normal (the absence of alpha-rhythm, the presence of slow waves). Clearly the deviations of the EEG are explained as neuro-dynamic disturbances, complicating the picture of this particular case of oligophehrenia.

In spite of the existence of general neurophysiological disturbances, the method of electro-encephalography can be used also for discovering localized centres of damage of the brain, which oligophrenics frequently have.

As we know, oligophrenia is a residual condition following diffuse damage to the central nervous system in the early stages of intra-uterine development or in the early period of life. Concordant with this is an observation that deviations in the EEG were distributed over all cortical areas in the majority of oligophrenics.

Along with this in many oligophrenics more or less clearly pronounced local changes are disclosed against the background of diffuse brain damage.

As an example we can study the wave record in Fig. 6.

The EEG was recorded from a pupil in the sixth class at the special school K. The medical record showed meningo-encephalitis with loss of consciousness. Delayed development was noticeable from an early age. A neurological examination revealed a diffuse symptomatology with a preponderance of damage in the motor

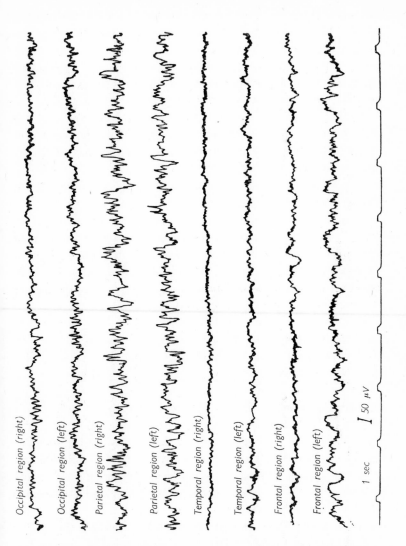

Occipital region (right)

Occipital region (left)

Parietal region (right)

Parietal region (left)

Temporal region (right)

Temporal region (left)

Frontal region (right)

Frontal region (left)

1 sec I 50 μV

FIG. 6. The EEG of a pupil in the 6th class of special school K (12 years old), with a diagnosis of „oligophrenia–imbecility". There are signs of a locus of pathological activity against a background of diffuse brain damage. Slow waves are apparent, predominantly in the central region, corresponding to a lesion in the motor analyser.

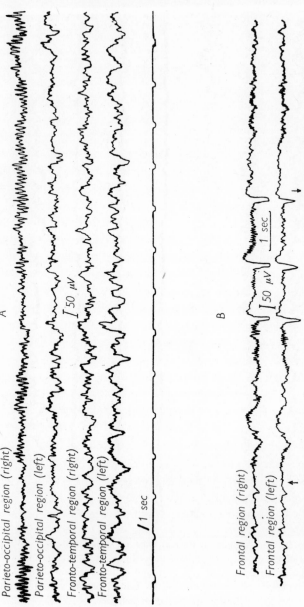

FIG. 7. (A) The EEG of a pupil in the imbecile class of special school E (13 years old). There are signs of a locus of pathological activity. The presence of slow pathological waves can be seen in the left hemisphere while the alpha-rhythm is relatively well preserved in the right hemisphere. (B) The EEG of a male pupil in the imbecile class M. A distorted response to a light stimulus, in the frontal regions of the cortex.

areas of the cortex. There were gross speech disturbances of an aphasic nature. Psychologically there was a general under-development of cognitive functioning. The EEG drew attention to the presence of pathological waves of large amplitude in various regions. The predominance of these large waves in the motor area accords with the clinical picture of damage to the motor analyser. The EEG in Fig. 7 can serve as another example. These waves were recorded from a schoolgirl in the imbecile class E (13 years old) whose neurological examination showed a locus in the left hemisphere, accompanied by a paralysis of the upper and lower extremities against a background of diffuse cortical damage. Conforming with this a gross locus of pathological activity in the left cerebral hemisphere was found in the EEG. The fact merits attention that many years after the brain trauma the electro-encephalogram shows the presence of clear signs of gross loci of pathological activity. The use of supplementary stimuli enables the detection of loci against the background of diffuse cortical damage. For example, slow pathological waves in all cortical areas were recorded from a pupil M. in the imbecile class. A light stimulus, which in normal children evokes a marked reduction in the amplitude of the emitted rhythm of electrical activity,—what is known as the depression of the alpha-rhythm—evoked in this case a singular distorted reaction in the form of a group of rhythmic oscillations the nature of which is evidence of the deep disturbance of the functional state (Fig. 7 B). This distorted reaction to the light is particularly evident in both frontal areas. Neurological examination of this boy revealed a localized bilateral fronto-subcortical symptomatology against a background of diffuse cortical damage. It is possible to detect loci of pathological activity in other cases of oligophrenia also, by means of functional overloading.

However, along with what has been described above it was also established that there is a relatively small section of mentally retarded children in whom the electrical currents differ only slightly from those of normal children and in these cases the utilization of the EEG for increasing the precision of the diagnosis is difficult. This points to the necessity of pursuing supplementary methods of investigation, which would be able to use the electro-encephalograph to obtain information about the functional state of the brain.

As has already been said, the results of the investigations of the cerebral electrical activity in normal and mentally retarded children given above were obtained under conditions of complete relaxation of the experimental subjects.

We used stimuli of flashing lights as a supplementary method which, in conjunction with the electrophysiological method, would enable a deeper study of the functional state of the brain in oligophrenia. The subject was made to lie on a divan in an isolated room. Half a metre in front of his eyes was an evenly illuminated screen on to which a pencil of light could be projected. The light stimulus was presented as rhythmic flashes of light of a frequency which varied between 3 and 24 flashes per second. A record of cerebral electrical activity was now produced, not only under conditions of relaxation, but also when a flashing light of different frequencies was involved.

Studies of the cerebral currents of normal children exposed to stimuli of light flashes showed that the normal cortex is able to modify the frequency of its electrical potentials (when exposed to the rhythmic light). Thus, for instance, if the oscillation frequency of the brain is 10 cycles per second (alpha-rhythm) under relaxed conditions, then under the influence of the flashing light at 14 cycles per second, the cortical rhythm will change its frequency, and the EEG graph will register oscillations with a frequency synchronous with the rhythm of the flashing light (14 cycles per second) instead of the alpha-rhythm (Fig. 8). This is characteristic of the functioning of the normal brain and is called the *re-organization* or *adoption* of a rhythm.

The well known Russian physiologist N. E. Vvedenskii considered that the ability of the nervous tissue to adopt the rhythm of impinging stimuli could characterize the functional state of this tissue.

For instance, a normally functioning nerve or nerve cell is capable of assimilating a high frequency of stimulation, but when the functional state is changed as a result of fatigue or an incurred

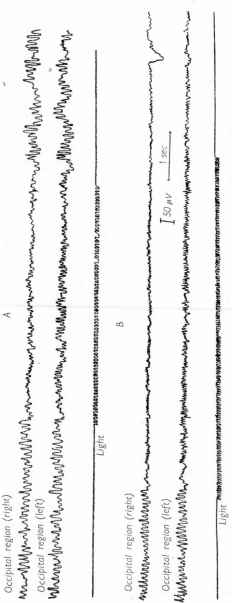

FIG. 8. (A) Subject V (14 years old). The adaptation of electrical waves in the occipital regions of the cortex to the rhythm of light flashes occurring 14 times a second. The initial frequency of the alpha-rhythm is 9.5–10 c/s. (B) Subject I (13 years old). The adaptation of electrical waves in the occipital cortical regions to the rhythm of light flashes occurring at a rate of 20 per sec. The initial frequency of the alpha-rhythm is 10 c/s.

FIG. 9. Subject V. K. Diagnosis "oligophrenia-imbecility". Stimulation by a light flashing with a frequency of 18 per sec. The adaptation of the corticalrhythm is absent.

illness, the nervous tissue loses its capacity to adopt high frequencies of stimulation. Whereas rhythmic stimuli of low frequency are easily adopted, high frequencies are responded to by the appearance of a rhythm of low frequency.

Investigations of cerebral electrical activity of mentally retarded children exposed to rhythmic light stimulation showed that the nature of the assimilation of the rhythm of the light flashes in oligophrenics is substantially different from that observed in normal children. Even in those cases where the EEG record of the mentally retarded child is taken under relaxed conditions and is not different from that of the normal child, the reaction of the cerebral cortex of the oligophrenic to the rhythmic light is substantially different from that of the normal cortex. When the normal child responds to flashing light stimulation of a high frequency (14–20 flashes per second) it is possible to observe a clear re-organization of the cortical rhythm as is shown in Fig. 8. However, in the majority of mentally retarded children this re-organization is usually either expressed very poorly or is completely absent.

This fact is demonstrated in Fig. 9 from which it can be seen that a rhythmic light stimulation of 14 cycles per second does not evoke any re-organization of the cortical rhythm.

In addition it is possible to observe that the majority of mentally retarded children differ from normal children in their clear assimilation of rhythms of low frequency (3–4 flashes per second), and also in the way in which slow waves appear on the EEG in response to flashes of high frequency. In Fig. 10A we can see the clear re-organization of the cortical rhythm to a light flash frequency of 5 cycles per second. In Fig. 10B we can see the appearance of slow waves on the record with a frequency of 3–4 cycles per second in response to a rhythmic stimulation with a frequency of 23 flashes per second.

All these peculiarities of re-organization in oligophrenics indicate substantial changes in the functional state of the brain and a significant disruption in neuro-dynamics, expressed as a tendency of the cortical cells to fall into a state of inhibition easily, and this appears as slow waves on the EEG.

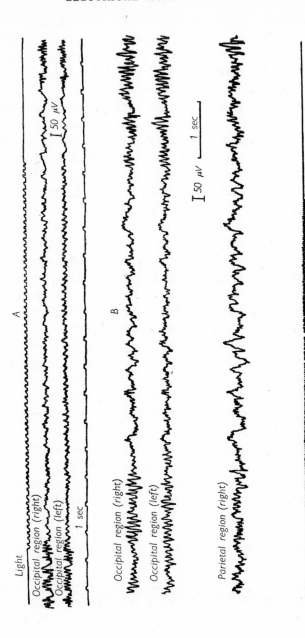

Fig. 10. (A) Subject S (13 years old). Diagnosis: "oligophrenia". A clear adaptation of the cortical rhythm to a frequency of 4 c/s. (B) Subject Sh. (14 years old). Electrical reaction of the cortex in response to the stimulation of a light flashing with a high frequency. The appearance of slow waves is recorded in the occipital and parietal regions.

The distinctive characteristics which mark the re-organization of the cortical rhythm in children with different types of mental retardation, reflect the degree of severity of the damage and the peculiarities of the structure of oligophrenic defect appearing in clinical investigations.

The electro-physiological method of investigation can also be used for gaining precision in a diagnosis of oligophrenia in those cases where this diagnosis is doubtful and requires additional corroboration. The possibility of using the method of electro-encephalography for diagnostic purposes can be illustrated by the following two examples: among the pupils in the 5th and 6th classes in a special school were four children who, according to the medical conclusion, were not oligophrenics and were subject to transfer to ordinary school. A study of the electrical currents of the brain showed that the cerebral electrical activity was fully preserved in three children, but departed slightly from the normal in one.

Clearly, in cases which are difficult to diagnose, the presence of a well expressed alpha-rhythm and the absence of pathological waves on the EEG argue against a diagnosis of oligophrenia. On the other hand poor expression of the alpha-rhythm and the presence of pathological waves on the EEG can corroborate a diagnosis of oligophrenia.

On just such grounds the electro-physiological method can be drawn upon to delimit oligophrenia from delays in development having a different origin. (See Chapter 1.)

During an examination of the children in the 1st class in a special school one of the pupils was found to show cerebral electrical activity of a completely normal character. After a time it transpired that this girl made successful progress in all subjects and in accordance with the medical conclusion she was diagnosed as suffering from delayed development and not from oligophrenia. As a result of quick compensation, this girl was sent to an ordinary general school. Many such examples could be given.

The method of electro-encephalography can also be used for the differential diagnosis of oligophrenia and deafness.

It is known that deafness appearing in early childhood can lead to general under-development in a child and that it can be a cause of diagnostic errors (see Chapter 2). Electro-encephalography establishes directly and objectively the characteristically functional condition of the brain and clearly it has a particular value in these cases. In Fig. 11 is the electro-encephalograph of a deaf girl C. (12 years old) who had studied for several years in a school for mentally retarded children. At 2, C. suffered from meningitis and did not speak until she was 5. General under-development was noticeable from an early age. When she was 8 she was mistakenly sent to a special school. Examination established that pronounced deafness was present and the secondary under-development of the intellect was caused by the deafness. The electrical activity of the brain showed a clearly expressed alpha-rhythm and an absence of any signs of a pathological state in the cerebral hemispheres. She was sent to a school for deaf children.

Electro-encephalography ought to be used for differentiating between oligophrenia and epileptic feeble-mindedness. Frequently in epileptic feeble-mindedness the EEG registers characteristic epileptic discharges, thus enabling a correct diagnosis. The EEG taken from child K. in Fig. 12 can serve as an example.

K. was 12 years old and had suffered from epileptic fits until she was 3. Until the examination a not very serious neurological symptomatology had been discovered—a poorly expressed hydrocephalus. K. was poor at spatial orientation, easily excited, periodically stupified, stammered, had no concept of number and could not communicate the sense of a narrative. Epileptic feeble-mindedness was the hypothetical diagnosis. In this case the formulation of the diagnosis was difficult because of the temporal remoteness of the fits which had been observed only until the fourth year of life. The presence of pronounced epileptic waves on the EEG confirmed the hypothetical diagnosis of epileptic feeble-mindedness.

The juxtaposition of the EEG and the clinical profile enables conclusions to be drawn about the correspondence between the extent of deviation in the electrical activity of the brain and the severity of the defect in oligophrenia.

It follows from the data presented that the character of the elec-

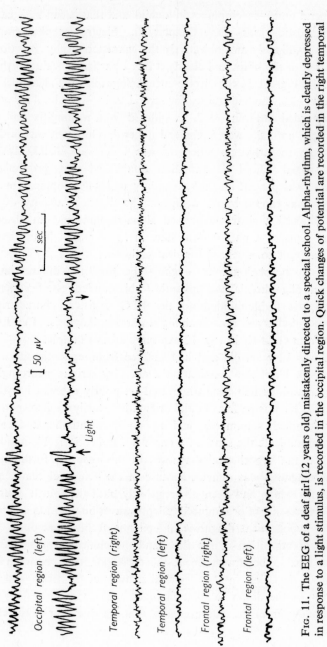

Occipital region (right)

Occipital region (left)

↑ Light

I 50 µV

1 sec

Temporal region (right)

Temporal region (left)

Frontal region (right)

Frontal region (left)

Fig. 11. The EEG of a deaf girl (12 years old) mistakenly directed to a special school. Alpha-rhythm, which is clearly depressed in response to a light stimulus, is recorded in the occipital region. Quick changes of potential are recorded in the right temporal region. Alpha-rhythm is registered in the frontal regions. The alpha rhythm is dominant in the occipital and frontal regions and the absence from the EEG of pathological waves attests the absence of organic disturbances of the brain.

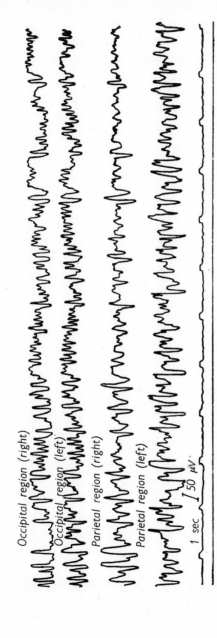

Fig. 12. Epileptic discharges can be seen on the EEG, indicating the presence of epilepsy in child K.

trical activity of the brain reflects not only the degree of the severity of the defect in oligophrenia, but also the qualitative uniqueness of the illness. All these observations allow us to conclude that the study of the electrical activity of the brain can be utilized as a supplementary method for investigating the clinical characteristics and diagnostics of oligophrenia.

CHAPTER 4

PECULIARITIES OF THE ORIENTATION REFLEXES IN CHILD-OLIGOPHRENICS

1. *Orientation Reflexes and Their Objective Indices*

The organism must be active in order to adapt correctly to the changing conditions of the environment and in order to orient itself successfully. It must discriminate and select those signals which are important for it and it must abstract these from the remaining unimportant stimuli.

If an animal is in a resting state and suddenly hears a strange noise, it immediately pricks up its ears and turns its head and eyes in the direction of the noise. If the noise is repeated, the animal turns its head again and may even stand and move over towards it. If, however, the noise is repeated several more times and nothing particular follows it, the animal will cease to react to it.

This is how the "orientation reflex" (or as I. P. Pavlov called it the "What's that?" reflex) manifests itself in its most simple and typical form. This reflex is evoked by a *new* stimulus and is displayed as an increase in the sensitivity of the sense organs and the arousal of a readiness to react to this stimulus. If the stimulus is accompanied by nothing (or as it is said, is not reinforced by the appearance of something having significance for the life of the organism, e.g. food or danger), it ceases to evoke a response from the organism. The orientation reflex to this stimulus is extinguished.

Physiological investigations, conducted in recent years, have enabled a full study of the basic mechanisms of the orientation reflex.

Electro-physiological experiments have shown that every stimulus, e.g. a light or a sound, always produces two currents in the brain. One of these—the specific—starts in the ganglia of the optic (or auditory) nerve and goes to the visual (or auditory) region of the cortex, leading to the arousal of specific (visual or auditory) reactions. Simultaneously another excitatory current develops: this arises when the excitation which has begun in the visual (or auditory) fibres arrives at its intermediate station, the brain stem or sub-cortical mechanisms of the brain. The excitation spreads over a particular accumulation of nerve cells known as the reticular formation and from here it spreads over the whole cortex, raises its tonus and puts all systems into a state of readiness for responses (Fig. 13). If the external stimulus is not accompanied by some effect which is significant for the organism, the excitation is extinguished, and the tonus of the cortex reduced. This second current of excitation which is aroused in the same way by any stimulus and is consequently of a non-specific character, is the physiological basis of the orientation reflex.

Physiological investigations have shown that the orientation reflex, which represents an active response of the organism to new stimuli, is manifested as a series of objective changes which can be traced.

The appearance of every new stimulus evokes a change in the electrical activity of the cortex (depression of the alpha-rhythm, see Chapter 3) as well as the directly observable turning to one side of the head and eyes. There is also a change in the electrical potentials of the skin (galvanic-skin reflex) which leads to a constriction of blood vessels in the extremities and their dilation in the head (this guarantees a reflex increase in the brain's blood supply). Finally it produces a change in respiration, cardiac activity and an increase in muscle tone. All these changes are observed for some time after the repetition of a stimulus, but when the stimulus is repeated several times without reinforcement, they disappear.

The character of the vascular reaction of the finger on the presentation of a weak light stimulus can serve as an example. As a response the blood vessels of the finger contract. When the stimulus is repeated several times, the response begins to weaken, and then gradually begins to disappear. The child habituates to the light which has no

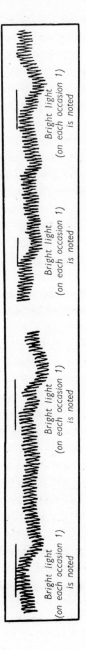

Fig. 13. The persistent preservation of the vascular component of the orientation reflex in a normal child when a stimulus having signalling significance is added (33—36 applications of a light signal).

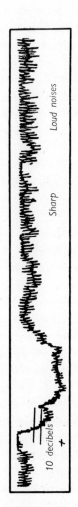

Fig. 14. The inhibition of responses to incidental stimuli on the action of a weak signalling stimulus (tone of 10 decibels).

7*

reinforcement and the orientation reflex becomes extinguished. If, however, the light is changed—becomes brighter or weaker, its colour or duration changes—the vascular reactions re-appear, indicating the recovery of the orientation reflex.

By using this method it is possible to study the orientation reflex, not only in those cases where it is aroused spontaneously by the action of a new stimulus, but also when it is specially activated and directed with the help of a verbal instruction. If we give a child the task of listening attentively for certain sounds, and then counting them or pressing a button in response to each one, we will again see the appearance of orientation reflexes. While the earlier mentioned vascular responses were preserved over 4–10 trials with identical stimuli, and then gradually became extinguished, in this case where the sound has become a signal for the child to make, a specific response, the responses are preserved much longer—over 20–40 trials.

The appearance of a good orientation reflex has yet another important consequence. A child who is concentrating his attention on the solution of a problem ceases to hear incidental stimuli. He does not react to the squeak of the door or to the noise outside the window. Stimuli which are not relevant to the problem with which he is occupied do not get through to him.

The selective nature of the orientation reflex can be recorded by objective methods we can describe. We give an example in Fig. 14. The child is presented with a series of weak sounds through headphones. He has to count them and every sound evokes a clear contraction of blood vessels in the finger—a component of the general orientation reaction. If, however, during this time there is a loud noise outside the window, there may be no orientation reflex to it. The incidental noise is not perceived and the vascular reactions to it are inhibited.

The presence of the orientation reflexes plays a large role in all the processes of higher nervous activity. Not one new temporary connection can be formed nor one new piece of knowledge or ability acquired without their participation.

To form a new connection it is essential to discriminate the

Fig. 15. The speedy extinction of the vascular component of the orientation reflex to a signal stimulus in a child-oligophrenic.

Fig. 16. The effect of an incidental stimulus in a child-oligophrenic.

given stimulus from a quantity of other stimuli. Only in such a case could it become a conditioned signal, capable of evoking an adequate responsive reaction. If there is no preliminary discrimination of the stimulus, a conditioned reflex to it cannot be formed.

This can be shown in one simple example.

We may give a child weak sounds and accompany each sound with the verbal instruction "Press the button". The experiment shows that it is sufficient to repeat this test 2–3 times for the child to begin pressing the button as soon as the sound is made and without waiting for the order.

Already after several repetitions a new connection is formed—the connection of the sound with the order to press the button with the finger. If during this time, we were to record the vascular or galvanic-skin responses of the child, we would confirm that every signal evokes an orientation reaction and that the orientation reaction is preserved after the formation of the connection just described.

We will now try to change the experiment somewhat. Initially we will present the child with monotonous sound stimuli for a protracted period without reinforcement by instructions. Gradually the child will habituate to them, they will lose all significance for him and the orientation reactions to them will be extinguished. After a strong extinction of the reflex to the sound stimuli we will try to re-establish a conditioned connection to them. For this we will begin to accompany each of the sounds with the order "Press the button". Now we obtain quite different results. For a long time the child continues to press the button only in response to the direct command. The connection between the sound and the order does not develop for a long time and the conditioned motor response to the sound is not re-established. The sound has become quite insignificant for the child and cannot be converted into a conditioned signal for a new supplementary connection. Only after a great number of reinforced repetitions—and only under these conditions—will the sound once more begin to evoke the orientation reaction and turn into a signal which can be connected with an order and evoke a conditioned reflex.

2. Orientation Reflexes in Child-oligophrenics

Many investigators have observed that the mentally retarded child has defects of attention. The French doctor and psychologist, Seguin, considered these defects of active attention the outstanding feature of the mentally retarded child and thought that if such a child could become actively involved in schoolwork and concentrate his attention on what the teacher required, he would not be mentally retarded.

Studies made in recent years enable an approach to an explanation of the elementary bases of attention in mentally retarded children.

Experiments in which vascular and galvanic skin responses were recorded showed that in a significant number of cases, stimuli of a low or medium intensity, which always evoke the orientation reflex in normal children, are not accompanied by such a reaction in child-oligophrenics. If orientation reflexes do occur, they are usually distinguishable by their considerably lower resistance to extinction. If the extinction of the orientation reflexes begins in normal children after 10 or 12 repetitions of the stimulus, then for a severely retarded child this response would occur for only 1 or 2 stimulus presentations and then abruptly extinguish (Fig. 15). It would not be correct to think that the mentally retarded child does not commonly react to repeated stimuli. A strong stimulus can evoke vascular and galvanic skin responses of unusual vigour and duration over many trials. They are clearly produced because of the participation of sub-cortical elements.

The orientation reflex of the mentally retarded child also has special characteristics when verbal instructions are the relevant stimuli.

The complications associated with organizing the fixation of attention to lessons in the mentally retarded child are probably connected with this important feature differentiating him from normal schoolchildren. We stated above that the directedness of attention of the normal schoolchild insures that all other irrelevant stimuli will not evoke orientation reflexes. With the mentally retarded child it is impossible to evoke a firm orientation reflex to stimuli presented, but nothing will prevent a switch of attention to all kinds of incidental stimuli.

The record in Fig. 16 shows how an irrelevant noise outside a window evoked a significant orientation reflex from a child, while the light signals in response to which the child was meant to press a button, did not evoke any component of the orientation reflex. Conversely, the great proneness to distraction of the mentally retarded child appears as an inability to maintain his attention.

Fundamental to this is the weakness and liability to fatigue of the cortical neural connections.

The disturbance of these stable orientation reflexes—observable in many mentally retarded children—results in serious changes in all forms of activity related to conditioned reflexes.

Later we will be specially concerned with the peculiarities of higher nervous functioning in the mentally retarded child. Here we are only interested in the peculiarities of the orientation reflexes.

If the mentally retarded child's responses to new stimuli extinguish after a few presentations of a stimulus or are absent from the start, can we expect to succeed in producing a quick and reliable formation of new conditioned associations to such a stimulus? Clearly not!

The instruction "Count the presented stimuli" does not evoke reliable responses to each stimulus from the mentally retarded child. The responses become only slightly more reliable and it is sufficient to repeat the same stimulus 4 to 8 times in succession, for the response to be extinguished. To see that this really is so may be easily seen if the child is posed a question. In this case the normal child who will count the presented signals will usually give correct answers. The mentally retarded child is unable to hold the instructions given and utters the first figure which comes into his head "50 ... or ... 100!" revealing that in general he has not counted the stimuli presented. In Fig. 17 an example of such an experiment is given.

It is possible to point out that in this instance the unreliability of the orientation responses of the child-oligophrenic does not depend only on the difficulty of committing the instructions to

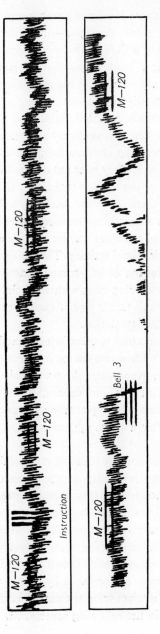

Fig. 17. The lack of a restoration of vascular responses after an instruction to count the beats of a metronome in a child oligophrenic. Reactions to strong incidental stimuli (bell) are preserved.

memory and executing them. If we give a more simple instruction—to press a button in response to the signal—the orientation responses extinguish just as quickly although the motor response is preserved to each signal. Such a simple instruction can be put into practice automatically without any increase in the child's level of activation. These facts are of interest for the understanding of the behavioural peculiarities of the mentally retarded child. One of the difficulties experienced in work at school is that very soon after the beginning of a lesson, mentally retarded children drop out of the class work and cease to take part in it. They hear but do not listen, they do not concentrate on the execution of their tasks, they cease to pay attention to them or carry them out "mechanically". The experiments we have just described show the elementary processes lying at the roots of the instability of the child's active attention which explains the many failures in their school training. The pathologically changed brain of the child is incapable of prolonged activity. He finds it difficult to become persevering even with the help of the teacher's verbal instructions and this fact is one of the most serious obstacles preventing his successful instruction.

If a mentally retarded child is asked when exactly he is to press the button he answers, "When you tell me it is necessary to press it." Apparently he does not even notice the presented signals and does not associate them with his movements. These facts are very reminiscent of the process of the generation of conditioned reflexes in the normal child after a thorough extinction of the orientation reflex.

This mechanical, unrecognized nature is typical of all connections which develop independently of the orientation reflex and we see below how characteristic this is of the production of new connections in mentally retarded children.

The instability of active attention fundamental to the swift extinction of the orientation reflexes in the mentally retarded child leads to the complex connections formed by him quickly extinguishing, being transformed and replaced by more primitive connections. These are quite distinct from the earlier, consciously formed connections as is seen in the following experiment.

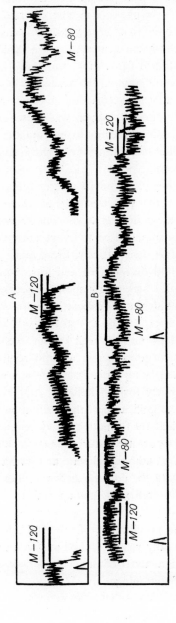

FIG. 18. A refusal to analyse stimuli and a transition to a stereotyped motor response "after one signal" in oligo-phrenia: A, an adequate motor response (a press to a metronome beat of 120 and no press to a beat of 80). B, the next press which is independent of the nature of the stimulus. The vascular responses to this disappear.

A child with extreme mental retardation was supposed to press a button in response to one signal (a metronome rate of 120 beats a minute) and not to respond to another signal (60 beats per minute). After some time the child reacted correctly to the signals. However, the procedure was continued for a short time and the child soon began to perform quite differently. He reacted to one signal and not to the next, these alternating reactions being stereotyped and completely independent of which signal was presented.

Why did the child, having begun to execute the instructions satisfactorily, suddenly fail to continue this performance but replace it with a mechanical stereotype?

The record, shown in Fig. 18, points to a possible cause of this phenomenon. Early on the presented signals evoked an active orientation reaction in the child and at this time his responses were correct. But the signals soon ceased to evoke such reactions and the child ceased to analyse them actively. From that time the selective reactions of the child disappeared and were replaced by the stereotyped reproduction of the two responses (positive and negative) which lost their differential association with the presented signals.

This closely reproduces the facts well known to the pedagogue that a weakness of active attention in a pupil results in correct answers disappearing and being replaced by the mechanical reproduction of some previously formed habit.

We have shown the significance of the orientation reflexes in a child's life and their role in the formation of new temporary connections. We have seen how they are disturbed in the mentally retarded child whose brain is in a pathological state and we have been able to acquaint ourselves with the consequences to which the unreliability of the orientation reflexes, fundamental to instability of attention, can lead.

We have studied the peculiarities of the establishment of new connections in the mentally retarded child and we can now transfer our attention to an analysis of the characteristic disturbances in his higher nervous functioning.

CHAPTER 5

PECULIARITIES IN HIGHER NERVOUS ACTIVITY OF CHILD-OLIGOPHRENICS

1. *Basic Regularities in the Development of Higher Nervous Functioning, Normal and Pathological*

In previous chapters we have touched upon several specific features of higher nervous functioning in child-oligophrenics. In the present chapter a series of other peculiarities in the dynamics of the nervous processes of these children will be examined.

Investigations into higher nervous functioning of child-oligophrenics were begun some thirty years ago.

Even the first investigations showed that there was a whole series of disturbances in the higher nervous functioning of oligophrenics. Many of these disturbances are observable in very early childhood in that these children deviate from the various indices characteristic of certain ages in the normal population.

The basic regularities and stages of normal development of higher nervous functioning were established in the investigations of N. M. Shchelovanova, N. I. Krasnogorskii, A. G. Ivanov-Smolenskii and others.

The child comes into the world possessing a series of unconditioned reflexes—innate response activities of the organism, aroused by the action of certain defined stimuli. These unconditioned reflexes are: sucking, clinging (the "ape" reflex), coughing, the protective eye-blink reflex and various others.

Even in the course of the first two weeks of life conditioned responses can be formed on the basis of these unconditioned reflexes.

Under natural conditions one of the first to appear is the conditioned sucking reflex which becomes established to the feeding situation (positioning in the arms of the mother, the mother's appearance) and is displayed, first of all, as sucking movements which are aroused when the child finds himself in this situation (i.e. when the mother takes him into her arms and puts him into position for feeding). Such a simple conditioned reflex is known as a natural conditioned reflex. An artificial conditioned reflex can also be established on the basis of the same unconditioned reflex. For example, by combining some auditory stimulus with the feeding, it is possible to obtain a conditioned sucking feeding response to the sound, after several combined repetitions. Somewhat later conditioned reflexes can be established on the basis of other weaker unconditioned responses, such as blinking.

In the course of the child's development, as well as the appearance of the conditioned reflexes, the unconditioned innate responses of the child themselves undergo a whole series of changes. These changes and the stages in which they can become diversified are connected with the developing cortex gaining more influence over unconditioned reflex activity. The unconditioned reflexes change in their appearance, are supplemented, and are "grown over" by the acquired conditioned reflexes which develop via them. Some of them are completely inhibited. For example, in the second month of life the primitive clinging reflex disappears and towards the end of the first year the sucking reflex ceases to appear. In the later development of the higher nervous functioning of the child the number of conditioned reflexes grows and they become more complex. Even more connections are formed on the foundation of the new, uniquely human, elements—with the participation of the second signalling system of words.

Significant deviations in reflex activity are observed in the very earliest stages of development in child-oligophrenics. In severe oligophrenics a reduction of the unconditioned feeding response can be observed. In very young oligophrenics natural conditioned reflexes are formed only slowly. To establish artificial conditioned reflexes is very difficult and in individual cases impossible.

Even in relatively slight cases of oligophrenia the normal manner in which unconditioned reflexes change is disturbed. Some of these, which normally disappear towards the end of the first year of life, are inhibited much later in child-oligophrenics. Parts of the unconditioned sucking reflex can sometimes be observed up to the second or third year of life. The clinging reflex is preserved considerably longer in child-oligophrenics than in normal children. In severe cases these primitive reflexes, such as the sucking reflex, may be quite uninhibited.

Particularly significant disturbances in child-oligophrenics are revealed in the very important process of the differentiation (discrimination) of stimuli.

Differentiation of stimuli develops in the following way: after the formation of a conditioned reflex to some stimulus (sound, light, or something else) another stimulus is introduced which begins to be employed with the first, but in its absence is not accompanied by the unconditioned reinforcement (e.g. food). At first the child reacts to this stimulus in the same way as he does to the conditioned signal. However, when he does not receive any reinforcement he begins to inhibit his responsive activity—he establishes a differentiation and distinguishes between the reinforced conditioned stimulus and the unreinforced differential stimulus.

Investigations of the early stages of the development of higher nervous activity of normal children have shown that the most simple differentiations can be established at 2–3 months, and that at 3–4 months the child can differentiate between two musical tones one octave apart.

It is quite different with child-oligophrenics. Even with a slight degree of oligophrenia such differentiations can only be established at a significantly later age. In cases of severe mental retardation the formation of a simple differentiation such as that between two tones separated by an octave may prove very difficult for children of 8 and 9.

Disturbances which are revealed in the later development of higher nervous functioning, especially those involving the establishment of more complex connections, will be similarly discussed later on.

The pathological changes in the higher nervous functioning of child-oligophrenics lead to noticeable disturbances in the functioning of all the analysers. An analyser, according to I. P. Pavlov, is an integral functional structure which comprises the peripheral sense organs, the unit of conduction (nerves) connecting the sense organ with the brain, and the cortical region where the analysis and synthesis of stimuli of a given modality takes place. The underdevelopment of the brain, and defects in neuro-dynamics associated with this, lead to some degree of disturbance in the cortical analysis and synthesis of stimuli impinging on the child. Moreover many child-oligophrenics exhibit disturbances in the functioning of their analysers, which are produced by defects in the peripheral parts of the analyser. In the sphere of vision such disturbances would be: disruption of refraction, nystagmus, squinting, disturbance of the transparency through the eye, and changes in the fundus of the eye.

Very many child-oligophrenics have defects in the motor analyser manifested as diverse disruptions in the motor system. In particular, delay in learning to walk has been observed in 50% of the pupils of special schools. Particularly frequent are disturbances in the functioning of the motor-speech analyser, i.e. disturbances in the analysis of the fine movements necessary for correct articulation. Diverse defects of speech are observed in many child-oligophrenics which disrupt their normal development. Delayed development was observed in 71% of pupils in special schools.*

The disturbances in speech development, which are constantly encountered by the teachers in the special schools in the course

* Data on the disturbances in functioning of analysers is put forward in the book by E. N. Pravdin-Vinarskii *Neurological Characteristics of the Oligophrenic Syndrome*, Moscow, A.P.N. R.S.F.S.R., 1957. The results are concerned with the composition of the pupils in special schools, but it is important to bear in mind that child-oligophrenics are a major unit making up this population.

of their instructing of child-oligophrenics, have a special significance among the disturbances in higher nervous functioning, observed in oligophrenics. I. P. Pavlov defined the basic methods of studying higher nervous functioning in man and pointed out that while in animals conditioned reflexes can be evoked by diverse direct stimuli from the environment (visual, auditory, olfactory, tactual, and other stimuli), in man conditioned responses can be evoked by the verbal symbols of real stimuli, as well as by the direct stimuli. Words become the signals of all objects and phenomena of the external world. According to I. P. Pavlov, the conditioned reflexes which are evoked by diverse directly perceived attributes of objects constitute the first signalling system of reality. This is common to man and animals. Responses to the verbal symbols of objects and their attributes and of real phenomena, and the ability to produce and use these verbal symbols, are the "extraordinary addition" to the higher nervous system, unique to man.

"Until the appearance of the family *homo sapiens*, animals interacted with the surrounding world only through the direct impressions of diverse factors, which acted on the various receptor organs of animals, the organs being connected with corresponding cells in the central nervous system. These impressions were unique signals of external objects.

"Later man appeared, and separated and improved immensely signals of a second order—signals of the primary signals. These were in the form of words which could be pronounced, heard, and seen. Finally these signals came to designate everything that people perceived directly in the external and in their internal worlds. They were used by people, not only for mutual communication, but also for private communication with themselves. The vast importance of words certainly explains the predominance of the new signals, although these words were and remain only the second signals of reality".*

* I. P. Pavlov. *Complete Collected Essays*, Vol. 3. Book 2, Moscow, Leningrad, A.N. U.S.S.R., 1951, 345 pages.

Words are stimuli for man which are as real as the attributes of objects and phenomena of the surrounding world and can evoke similar responses from him.

However, the most important characteristic of words does not lie in their possible use as *substitutes* for conditioned stimuli (it is possible to establish responses to words even in animals) but in that they introduce a new principle into higher nervous functioning—*the principle of abstraction and generalization*.

The mastery of verbal speech enables man to discriminate the important and substantial features of objects and phenomena, and abstract these from the insignificant non-significant features. It enables him to develop a generalized knowledge of reality and to create historical experience which can be preserved in words and language.

With the development of the second signalling system the first signalling system changes, and the formation of connections between directly perceived stimuli takes place with the participation of the second signalling system. Thus the investigations of the colleagues of Academician K. M. Bykov show that verbal effects can extend through conditioned reflexes even to the functioning of the internal organs.

Since the second signalling system has such significance for higher nervous functioning it is natural that a disturbance in its development cannot but tell on all manifestations of higher nervous functioning in the child-oligophrenic. On the other hand, disturbances in the second signalling system do not arise directly. As I. P. Pavlov has indicated, the second signalling system is a product of the same nervous network as the first system and the same pathological changes in the state of the brain and the disturbances in neuro-dynamics connected with such changes lie at the root of disturbances in both systems. It needs to be noted, however, that the pathological changes in the brain in oligophrenia tell considerably on the developments of the more complex activity of the brain, that which supports speech activity, and they lead to a drastic disturbance in this activity.

2. *Some Peculiarities of the Dynamics of the Nervous Processes in Child-oligophrenics*

Disturbances of the neuro-dynamics* in child-oligophrenics are discovered even in the most simple aspects of higher nervous activity, in simple conditioned connections. In the present chapter fundamental peculiarities of the higher nervous functioning in child-oligophrenics will be described. These peculiarities have been demonstrated in investigations carried out in recent years.

The results obtained from studying higher nervous functioning in child-oligophrenics between 9 and 12 years of age and in classes I to III of an auxiliary school will be reported. Initially the most general characteristics discriminating all the children will be given. Developmental changes of higher nervous functioning and also the differences between various clinical groups of oligophrenics will be noted.

Conditioned motor responses with verbal re-inforcement† can be used as a basic reaction, forming a basis for the production of all conditioned and differential reflexes. When investigating higher nervous activity by this means the technique often used is the squeezing of a rubber bulb upon the direct verbal command "Press". As opposed to salivary excretion in response to food, used for investigations based on salivary conditioned reflexes, or vascular constrictions in the hand in response to applied cold, used in work related to the vascular motor conditioned reflex method, pressure on a bulb is not an unconditioned reaction. The reaction of pressing the bulb in response to the word "Press" appears early (when the word's meaning is mastered) and remains permanent in the developmental experience of a child, but it is only stable within the compass of the

---

* By neuro-dynamics or the dynamics of the nervous processes is mean the processes involved in excitation and inhibition and their interaction.

† This method, introduced by A. G. Ivanov-Smolenskii, was described in his book *The Methodology of Studying Human Conditioned Reflexes*, Moscow, 1933. More detailed basic data obtained by these methods with child-oligophrenics are given in the book *Problems of Higher Nervous Functioning in the Normal and Anomalous Child*, Moscow, A.P.N R.S.F.S.R. Vol. I, 1956.; Vol. II, 1958.

present method in which it is to some degree equivalent to unconditioned reflexes.

Before proceeding to the production of new conditioned associations it is customary to observe how the initial response is executed.
In child-oligophrenics it is distinguished by its several peculiarities.
First of all, at the beginning of the investigations the child-oligophrenic's response is accentuated; having squeezed the bulb, the
child does not relax his grip immediately. While for normal children
of a similar age the press is short and lasts between 0·5 and 1·5
seconds, for oligophrenics the response continues 3–5 times longer
and frequently they only release their grip after an order such as
"Let go!" (see Fig. 19). Investigations show that this is not so much

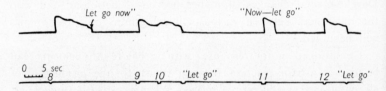

FIG. 19. The tonic character of the reactions of a child-oligophrenic (Natasha M.,
12 years old). The upper line is the record of the motor responses. The lower
line is a record of the verbal orders "Press" and "Let go".

through a failure to understand the task, as through the peculiarities of the neuro-dynamics of child-oligophrenics: even after
a detailed explanation to the effect that the bulb should be squeezed
when the order is given and then quickly released and after a demonstration of the required presses, the child cannot regulate his movements correctly and his responses do not immediately become
similar to those we observe in the normal child. His responses are
rigidly abrupt and approach a definite constant magnitude, not
changing later, and only by degrees under training. In some children this tonicity or "tightening" appears in the course of several
dozen responses. Prolonged manifestations of this tonicity of
responses is a consequence of inertness, of the high inertia of excitation in the motor analyser. The occurrence of motor perseveration is another indication of inertness in the motor analyser. If the

order "Press" is given several times with short intervals between each order (1 or 2 seconds) and then the order is discontinued, the children continue to press the bulb several times in the same rhythm as that in which the orders were given (see Fig. 20).

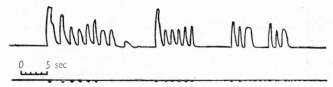

0   5 sec

FIG. 20. Superfluous movements of a perseverative nature in oligophrenia (Zoya P., 13 years old). The upper line is a record of the motor responses. The lower line is a record of the verbal order "Press".

The third peculiarity of the motor responses of child-oligophrenics is the acute disturbance in the stabilization of these responses. The strength, duration, and latency period of their motor reactions acquire a constant and steady size extremely slowly. The movements of these children remain disorganized for a long period of time, while those of the normal child of 8 or 9 acquire a steady character, and become even in form, duration and strength (see Fig. 21). This acute slowing down of the stabilization process of responses is produced by disturbances in the concentration of the excitatory process and its increased tendency to irradiation.

Yet another peculiarity of their motor responses is connected with the increased irradiation of excitation when the internal inhibition is weak: the presence of inter-signal responses, i.e. of responses which are not attached to the time sequence of the signals, but which arise in the pauses between signals (the orders "Press") (see Fig. 22). Such responses are not observed at all in normal children of the same age.

The control of the motor responses in relation to the direct command anticipates the production of a new positive conditioned response. A defined conditioned signal (for example the flashing of a light or a sound) is given, which reinforces the order "Press" in the second or third second. In this way a new conditioned stimulus is combined with the one previously established in the child (in his previous experiment). This is evoked by the reinforcement and is just as strong as it would be to the unconditioned stimulus. After several such combinations the child begins to press the bulb before the reinforcement of the signal by the order.

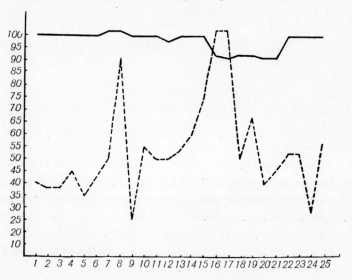

FIG. 21. The constancy of magnitude of the motor responses of a normal school child (N. K. 12 years old) (the continuous upper line) and the oscillation of magnitude of responses in a child-oligophrenic (Valerii S., 11 years old) (the lower hatched line). The horizontal axis records the number of the conditioned response. The vertical axis records their magnitude.

Earlier a series of investigators had shown (V. N. Osipov and others) that the speed with which conditioned responses are established to verbal reinforcement is not on average lower in child-oligophrenics than in their normal peers. These results have been confirmed

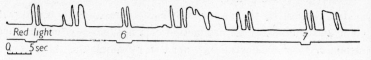

FIG. 22. The high frequency of inter-signal responses in a child-oligophrenic (Valerii S., 11 years old). The upper line is the record of motor responses. The lower line is the record of conditioned signals.

in later investigations. In feeble-minded children conditioned responses are usually established after 1 or 2 combined presentations of the conditioned stimulus and the reinforcement. Only when the mental retardation is more severe (imbeciles) has the establishment of such responses been slower. This was in a series of cases. A study of child-imbeciles who were not being instructed in special schools showed that in some of them conditioned reflexes to verbal reinforcement could not be produced, while with idiots conditioned reflexes either could be established on the basis of unconditioned reinforcement only with very great difficulty or not at all.

How are we to explain the fast and quite normal production of conditioned responses in the child-oligophrenics (feeble-minded and some imbeciles) studying in the special schools?

Observations show that the formation of these conditioned responses in the normal child of 5 or 6 occurs with the active participation of the verbal system of speech, in which occur the formation of general verbal connections of the type, "When there is a light, it is necessary to press." These general connections of a cortical type are distinct from the conditioned connections in animals and comprise a basic stock of experience acquired by man.

It is clear that even in the presence of certain pathological deviations from normal (for example, relatively slight degrees of oligophrenia) simple temporary connections of the described type of conditioned responses to simple signals with verbal reinforcement are produced with the active participation of the verbal system. This speeds up the establishment of the connection, levels out individual differences in neuro-dynamics and leads to the quick production of these conditioned responses. It is necessary to observe, however, that simple conditioned connections can be formed without the participation of the second signalling system. Investigations conducted with a series of higher animals have shown that it is possible to establish conditioned responses to simple stimuli after 3–5 or even fewer combined presentations.

In the presence of considerable pathological changes, when the extent of the second signalling system and its interaction with the first system are severely disrupted—as is the case with severe forms of mental retardation (imbecility and idiocy)—the establishment of even simple connections is slowed down because of the absence of the influence of the verbal system which naturally accelerates such connections being formed and because of the disturbances in the "locking" activity i.e. because of the disturbance of the elementary forms of neural synthesis.

If, however, the *formation* of simple positive connections in feeble-minded oligophrenic children is not disrupted, then the *stabilization* of the established conditioned responses proceeds as slowly as the stabilization of motor responses obtained by direct verbal orders.

Somewhat greater disturbances are observed in the production of simple differentiations than in the formation of positive conditioned connections. For producing differentiation, another light signal (e.g. a blue light) is introduced along with the positive signal (e.g. a yellow light) and the appearance of the additional stimulus is given negative reinforcement, "Don't press." In response to the positive signal the child has to press the bulb and in response to the supplementary stimulus he has to inhibit the movement and withhold his response. While these simple differentiations are usually established by a healthy child of 8 or 9 after one or two combined presentations of the differential signal and the order "Don't press", for many child-oligophrenics 3–5 or even more presentations are necessary.

However, in the majority of child-oligophrenics to the degree of feeble-mindedness and imbecility, simple differentiations are established on the basis of the combined action of the first and second (verbal) signalling systems, just as with normal children. The manner of the formation of these simple inhibitory connections has only quantitative differences dependent on a certain weakness in the internal inhibition of oligophrenics.

Only in individual feeble-minded and imbecile children is the formation of simple differentiations considerably slowed down (requiring more than 5 joint presentations) and this occurs when there are signs of disturbance in the participation of the verbal system (the absence of adequate verbal report is a primary sign of this).

To establish such differentiation in severe imbeciles requires several dozen combined presentations, while in idiots, as has been already said above, even positive conditioned reflexes cannot be established with verbal reinforcements.

Differentiation in severely retarded children can be established using other forms of reinforcement (e.g. unconditioned food reinforcement) and is also very difficult.

The consolidation of differentiation in feeble-minded children is disrupted. While a differentiation in normal children is stable from the moment it first appears and regularly appears in the future, in many oligophrenics it is repeatedly inhibited and remains unstable for a long time.

In this way the stamping in of an inhibitory connection is insufficient for the regular appearance of the corresponding differential associations in the actions of the child-oligophrenic. Sometimes he responds with impulsive reactions to an inhibitory signal instead of completely abstaining from any movement. In some children the impulsive reactions are so great that it is difficult to judge whether or not a differential association exists (Fig. 23).

The somewhat slower than normal production of differential associations in many child-oligophrenics and the reduced rate at which these become stable in a substantial number of children indicate the weakness of their internal inhibition.

One further peculiarity in the higher nervous functioning of child-oligophrenics is noticeable in the production of these first differential associations—wide generalization of stimuli (lack of difference in significance). This is shown by the fact the majority of child-oligophrenics will respond to all introduced signals with the same response as that with which they respond to the established conditioned reaction, regardless of the extent to which these signals differ from the positive signal. After a conditioned reaction has been established to a yellow light signal children respond with a similar press of the bulb in response to a blue or green light, and in many cases to a sound, whistle, and even to

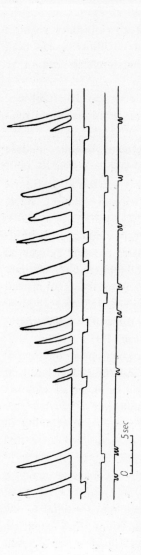

Fig. 23. Impulsive responses to a differential signal (a female pupil of a special school, Alla R., 9 years old). The record of the motor responses is the top line. The second line is the record of the positive signal (a green light). The third line is a record of the differential signal (a red light). On the bottom line is the record of the verbal reinforcement (a double mark represents "correct", and a treble mark, "Don't press").

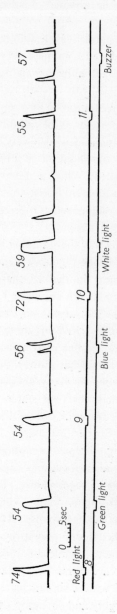

Fig. 24. The wide generalization of stimuli in an oligophrenic school child (Vitya B., 14 years old). The top line is a record of the motor responses. The second line is a record of the conditioned stimulus. The bottom line is a record of newly introduced stimuli.

a rap (Fig. 24). It is only in some child-oligophrenics that generalization is relatively limited so that auditory stimuli introduced
to an established conditioned response to a light stimulus do not
result in generalization and evoke a positive response.

The pathologically extensive irradiation of excitation lies at
the root of the stimulus generalization (diffuse generalization) of
child-oligophrenics. In the presence of a stimulus the process of
excitation is aroused at some point in the cerebral hemispheres,
but it is not concentrated there (as it is in the normal brain); it
irradiates and diffuses over neighbouring regions (even to relatively distant cortical areas). As a result of this, new stimuli, going
to these more distant parts of the cortex, are connected with the
positive signal and evoke the same response. Such broad irradiation of the excitatory process is never observed in normal children
of this age. In these children a positive signal only generalizes to
similar stimuli.

Yet another peculiarity in the higher nervous functioning of
child-oligophrenics appears during the first presentations of new
stimuli after a conditioned response to some signal has been established. Many new or unfamiliar stimuli, particularly strong stimuli,
produce an inhibition of responses to subsequent conditioned
signals—external inhibition. Disinhibition of differentiation is more
frequently observed. External inhibition of conditioned responses
and the disinhibition of differential responses bear witness to the
insufficient stability of the conditioned connections in child-oligophrenics. An example of internal inhibition is differential inhibition which is an active process and is produced as a result of
defined nervous tension. In contrast, external inhibition is passive
and arises spontaneously under defined conditions (for example,
from the action of a strong incidental stimulus) without any establishing process. As has been mentioned above it can be expressed
not only in the inhibition of established conditioned responses,
but also conversely, in the appearance of responses to inhibitory
signals, i.e. in fact in any conditioned reflex situation which is
disrupted in some way. A simple example of external inhibition
is the cessation by school children of their activities for some time,

when someone comes into the classroom during a lesson or when there is a loud noise somewhere outside the classroom. Thus one of the manifestations of external inhibition is the distraction of attention.

External inhibition is more strongly pronounced in child-oligophrenics than in normal children. In individual cases the application of a strong incidental stimulus inhibits responses to conditioned signals right to the end of a given experiment, i.e. acts for several minutes. In other cases there is no protracted inhibition of the conditioned responses; sometimes the conditioned responses to the positive signals are not inhibited at all,—the child-oligophrenic begins to respond with a positive reaction to the differential stimuli following the incidental stimuli, i.e. the differentiation is disinhibited. Such significant features of external inhibition are not observed in normal children and an incidental stimulus may affect only the first positive differential signal following the incidental stimulus. The strong external inhibition of child-oligophrenics is connected with the peculiarities of their orientation responses which have been described above.

We will not discuss the facts associated with the incomplete participation of speech in the process of the formation of new connections now. This will be done in a subsequent chapter. Here we will only consider some features of the verbal reports of child-oligophrenics concerning the development of conditioned responses to visual or auditory signals and concerning the development of simple differentiations. The verbal report, in the form of answers to questions put by the experimenter, provides an opportunity for analysing the perception and verbalization by the children of the conditioned reactions and differentiations which are being established. The results of many investigations have shown that normal school children between 8 and 10 can recount correctly how the signals have been used, what response they make to these signals and why to some signals they press the bulb and to others they do not. Thus, normal children of this age can adequately verbalize the signals, the responses, the connection between the responses and the signals and the connection between the signals,

responses, and reinforcement, i.e. all the elements of simple conditioned connections. Child-oligophrenics cannot do this. Feeble-
minded children can name the presented signals correctly and can
answer correctly when asked what they are doing, but in some
cases the connection between the signals and the responses is
misrepresented by them. In their reports they switch the order
of the signal and the response and claim that first of all they pressed
and then the light came on, or that they pressed and thereby switch-
ed on (lit) the light. In this alteration of the verbal report can be
seen a concordance with certain connections which have been
repeatedly reinforced in the past experience of the child: the pressing
of a button makes a bell ring, the turning of a switch produces the
lighting up of a bulb, etc. These old established connections prevent
a correct reflection of connections now being formed, and these are
altered to accord with the old, habitual, stereotyped forms. Such
alteration is a consequence of the inertness of the old stereotyped
connections in the presence of the unstable new ones against a background of an insufficiently active use of the verbal system in the
formation of new conditioned responses. It is observed in some
children and it is shakily overcome according to the stability of
new conditioned responses or during the establishing of a second
analogous conditioned connection.

Disturbances in reflective accounts of the connection between
the signal, response, and the reinforcement are significantly more
serious and more widely deviant from the norm: when he has
established the conditioned response to the signal which is reinforced by the command "Press!", the child cannot say why he
pressed and instead of naming the real direct reason—the command—he names some other reason formally associated with a
signal which has been used previously, or is similar, or he completely refuses to give an explanation. Thus for example, one pupil
in the 2nd class of a special school established a conditioned response
to a green light and explained his actions, "I pressed on the green
because when it is green the traffic can go." Subsequently a conditioned response was established to a red light and he then said,
"I pressed on the red, because when it is red the pedestrians can

cross." Thus in these cases we have a utilization of elements from past experience which are, however, used inadequately and in a stereotyped manner. They are produced quite independently of the conditions under which the new temporary connection has been established,

Even more frequent are verbal reports of the following type: "I pressed because it was green." When asked why it is necessary to press when it is green, the children usually answer that they do not know. Analogous reports are given when differentiations are being established.

The real reason for the absence of a response to an inhibitory signal is not given by the children.

Thus disturbances in the combined functioning of the first and second signalling systems are revealed when child-oligophrenics of the mentioned age express simple conditioned connections in verbal form. These disturbances are not related to the visual and immediately given elements of conditioned connections (the signal, the response), but to the more covert, less perceptible elements (the connection between the conditioned signal and the response and particularly the connection between the responses to a signal and the reinforcement) or in other words—the conditioned meaning of the signals.

In the most simple cases these disturbances are easily overcome when the conditioned connections are re-established. They can remain extremely persistent if more complex connections are being established, as we will see below.

We have already noticed signs of a certain weakness of internal inhibition in child-oligophrenics. These were seen in the production of simple differentiation. This weakness of internal inhibition, characteristic of child-oligophrenics, emerges more strongly when the child encounters more difficult problems. The differentiation of light (or sound) stimuli which are alike in colour (or tone and timbre) but which differ in intensity, proceeds much more slowly in child-oligophrenics than in normal children. The production of a differentiation to a dark red light after a positive conditioned response to a light red light has been established can serve as an example. This differentiation is established more slowly by child-oligophrenics than one where the differentiation is according to colour, and it becomes stable much more slowly. In the majority of these children differentiation according to intensity does not become absolutely stable. Frequently it is sufficient to present two or three inhibitory stimuli in succession to bring about the disinhibition of the differentiation and the child begins to respond to the inhibitory signal as though he cannot discriminate it from the positive signal (Fig. 25). This easy disinhibition of differentiations is only observed in severe oligophrenics when simple differentiations by colour are being established.

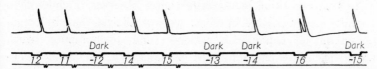

FIG. 25. The disinhibition of a differentiation based on the intensity of a light signal upon the presentation of two differential signals successively (Sasha Z. 9 years old). The top line shows the motor responses. The second line is a record of the stimuli (a bright red light is the positive signal, a dark red light is the inhibitory signal). The bottom line is a record of the verbal reinforcement "Correct".

The disturbances of verbal reports during the production of differentiations according to intensity extend to the verbal description of current signals. In a series of cases child-oligophrenics in whom a differentiation had been established said, "When it was red, I pressed, while when it was also red, I did not press." However, these disturbances are not persistent and when differentiation has become stable it is usually possible to obtain an adequate verbal answer similar in form to that which normal schoolchildren would give in the same situation.

*   *

*

So far we have only considered those peculiarities observed in child-oligophrenics when relatively simple systems of connections are being established: where the differences between the positive and the inhibitory stimuli are large and extremely easy to see (e.g. the difference between a red and a blue light). In the child's real life, especially in school, such simple new connections are established rather rarely. Most of the connections being established are much more complex and abstract. Complex connections are established in the course of learning grammar, arithmetic, and in the child's assimilation of other school knowledge and skills. In the establishment of these connections the significance of signals is embodied in attributes which frequently have no direct and simple visual character and whose discrimination is achieved easily only with the help of speech.

For an exposition of the disturbances observed in child-oligo-phrenics under these conditions, we will analyse the production of systems of conditioned responses and differentiation which are sufficiently complex to serve as models of the complex connections mentioned above and which are at the same time sufficiently simple for physiological analysis to be attainable.

The differentiation of signals varying in temporal duration can serve as an example of such a system. In this experiment the positive conditioned response is established to a brief light signal (1–1·5 sec), while a somewhat longer signal (lasting 5–6 sec) is reinforced negatively by the command "Don't press!" For all other stimulus qualities (colour and intensity in the case of light signals; tone, timbre, and intensity in the case of auditory signals) the positive and inhibitory reactions remain identical. To establish this differentiation the child needs to turn his attention away from the attributes of intensity and of colour (which is the most directly visible aspect of light signals), and separate out the attribute of duration, which is the real signal and lies at the basis of the differ-entiation.

For normal schoolchildren between 8 and 10 this differentiation is established after 4–6 combined presentations of the inhibitory signal and the negative reinforcement "Don't press!" Simulta-neously with the appearance of the differentiation in the motor responses, adequate verbal reports of the connection between the signals and the reinforced responses are given by these children, i.e. they formulate a rule of action verbally. The formation of this differentiation in child-oligophrenics presents another picture: the establishment lingers on for 15–20 combined presentations of the differential signal and the reinforcement "Don't press!" The differentiation is formed gradually. The response to the inhibitory signal waveringly decreases to nothing, but even when the child first completely witholds his press to the differential signal, his verbal report remains inadequate, while the differentiation is unstable and easily disinhibited, particularly if the reinforcement is eliminated.

An analogous picture is presented in the establishment of differentiations based on the principle of correct alternation of positive and differential signals. For example, light signals of a green colour, of identical intensity and duration may be presented the whole time: the first and second signals are reinforced positively with the order "Press!", but the third is reinforced by the order "Don't press!", while the next two signals are again reinforced with the command "Press!" and the same green light following these is accompanied by the negative reinforcement. Thus, the differential signals are distinguished from the positive signals only by their position in a series of other identical stimuli—only by their ordinal number. All visual attributes of the signals have no significance in this case and it is necessary to turn attention away from these attributes for a correct differentiation of the stimuli.

In a normal child of 8 or 9 this type of differentiation is established about as quickly as the differentiation based on duration. An adequate verbal account can be obtained from the moment the differentiation is established and this attests the active participation of speech in the process. Differentiations by alternation proceed much more slowly in child-oligophrenics than in normal children and possess a series of characteristics which are noticeable in the production of differentiation according to duration and which attest to the insufficient participation of speech in the formation of these connections.

When I. P. Pavlov was comparing the production of conditioned

9

connections, formed on the principle of correct alternation of the positive and inhibitory signals in the healthy adult human being and animals, in which the formation of such connections are almost impossible, he noticed that the establishment of this type of connection was very easy for man because he "counts and possesses the concept of number".*

Indeed even during the pre-school period the verbal system is participating in the establishment of conditioned connections in healthy children and it is because of this that the child can generalize the stimuli acting on him, refer them to defined categories, and can consequently easily discriminate those signs which are real signals. When verbal generalization is utilized, connections are formed quickly (usually in leaps and bounds) and they are stable. Most complex connections are established quickly on the basis of speech in children of school age and in adults.

The formation of complex connections proceeds quite otherwise in child-oligophrenics. Because of the under-development of the brain and the associated neuro-dynamic disturbances, the speech of these children cannot take a full part in the establishment of even relatively simple connections. Deficiencies associated with the participation of speech appear in the course of the formation of complex connections and in the establishment of complex differentiation.

One of the most important indications of the disturbance of the active participation of the second signalling system in the establishment of differentiation is that children cannot usually recount correctly to which signals they give responses and they usually say something about the establishment of one of the preceding and more firmly fixed connections. For example, if the differentiation of red light signals according to duration is established after the differentiation of signals by intensity (light) then child-oligophrenics give the following account. "When it was light (in colour) I pressed, but when it was dark I did not press", although the signals were all equally bright. It should be noted that even

* *Pavlovian Methods*, Moscow, A.N. U.S.S.R., Vol. 2, 246 pages.

if the instructions indicate that all the signals appearing are equally light (or equally dark) this does not lead to a correct verbal account. A correct verbal formulation can be obtained only after a direct instruction to the effect that the signals differ in duration and that it is necessary to act in accordance with their duration. It should be noted that the longer the period over which differentiation is established and verbally formulated to produce stability, the more inert does the supplementary verbal connection become and the more difficult it is for the speech activity of the oligophrenic to be included into the analysis of a relatively complex system of connections which is to be established subsequently.

Analogous disturbances in reports are observed in the establishment of conditioned responses requiring a correct alternation with differentiations—for example in the establishment of conditioned responses to every second signal or to two signals with differentiation to every third signal. If such systems of connections are formed after the differentiation of signals according to intensity, then when the new system of connections is apparent in the responses, the verbal report remains as it was in the establishment of the differentiation according to intensity ("I pressed to the light, but did not press to the dark", or vice versa). The new signalling attribute is not discriminated in the child's speech. If conditioned responses to every second signal are established after a differentiation according to stimulus intensity, then when this latter was established and correctly cognized and formulated in the response (this can be achieved under defined conditions), the verbal account of the establishment of conditioned responses to every second signal also corresponds to the previous system of connections and the children continue to say, "When it was small (or short) I pressed, but when it was large (or long) I did not press." Such verbal reports show the sharply pronounced inertness of the stereotypes consolidated earlier and stabilized verbally. This inertness is one of the most important reasons for the disturbances in the participation of the verbal system in the establishment of new connections in oligophrenia. The establishment of new relatively complex connections proceeds—as if mechanically—by means of a protracted "beating in". The inertness, "the sluggish lability" of the mental processes of child-oligophrenics is also noticeable in psychological investigations. It is constantly necessary to combat the appearances of inertness in the instruction of child-oligophrenics in special schools.

The inertness of the nervous processes in the establishment of relatively complex connections in child-oligophrenics is revealed in the way in which systems of connections which have been established without adequate verbal explanation by the child are extremely lifeless and sluggish.

Simple systems of connections which have been established in child-oligophrenics with the participation of speech can be easily changed and changed around. Thus if a positive conditioned response has been established in the child to a red light signal and a differentiation to a green light, this system of connections can be formulated verbally by the child, so that it is sufficient to combine one or two presentations of a formerly inhibitory signal with positive reinforcement ("Press!"), in order for consistent responses to appear to it, and simultaneously the child is able to say that he is now performing in a reversed manner. The conditioned significance of a previously positive signal can be changed just as quickly and if it is accompanied by the negative reinforcement "Don't press!", it speedily acquires an inhibitory significance and the child ceases to respond to it.

It is quite otherwise with child-oligophrenics when a change in relatively complex connections established mechanically without a correct verbal formulation is made. They change with very great difficulty, and sometimes after several dozen combined presentations they remain unstable and the new differentiation [is easily disrupted (Fig. 26). In some cases the system of connections is re-established when reinforcement is withdrawn.

As was shown in the investigations of I. P. Pavlov and his collaborators, the speed of transference of the conditioned significance of stimuli is one of the main indices of the lability of nervous processes.

The study of the transfer of diverse systems of connections

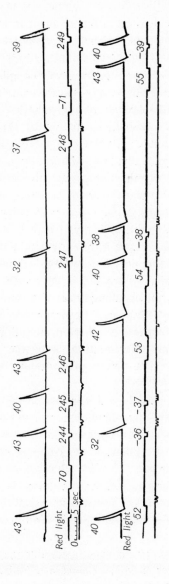

FIG. 26. The inertness of the initially established conditioned connections, manifested during a change (a female pupil in a special school, N.E., 13 years old). In both extracts from the recordings, the top line is a record of the motor responses, the second line, a record of the conditioned signals. The bottom line is a record of the reinforcement (a double pulse indicates "correct", a single pulse, "Press", and treble pulse "Don't press"). The upper extract is before the change. The lower extract is during the process of the change.

in child-oligophrenics shows that the lability of the nervous processes is close to normal only in the most simple system of connections (about which the child can give an adequate verbal report). The decrement in the lability of the nervous processes and their inertness is revealed in the transfer of complex connections.

When the establishment of simple and relatively complex systems of connections is compared it can be seen that the complex systems of connections in child-oligophrenics possess a series of specific features: (1) they do not obtain adequate verbal expression in the verbal accounts of a child; (2) they are established slowly; (3) they become stable gradually and significantly more slowly than simple connections; (4) they are easily disinhibited when reinforcement is withdrawn, when there is a break in the experiment, and when incidental stimuli occur; (5) they are inert and can be transferred only with difficulty.

All these features, demonstrated in recently conducted investigations,* are indicative of connections established without the full participation of the verbal system and in the presence of a disturbance in the joint activity of signalling systems. A similar manner of establishing conditioned responses to proprioceptive stimuli (stimuli from the internal organs) is observed in healthy children or in the formation of fine differentiations when the differences between the positive and inhibitory signals cannot be verbally specified.

The strong influence of pathological inertness on the formation of new connections in child-oligophrenics forces us to pose the question of the possibilities of its being overcome and the problem of improvements of the perception of the complex connections being established by children.

Specially designed experiments show that there is a method which facilitates an acceleration of the establishment of the complex systems of connections just mentioned. It is most important to

* These features were analysed in the investigations of V. I. Lubovskii, A. I. Meshchiakov, and N. P. Paramonova, conducted in the Institute of Defectology A.P.N. R.S.F.S.R.

obtain an adequate verbal account immediately the differentiation has been established. It is possible to achieve this, when a new conditioned signal has been applied for the formation of a differentiation according to stimulus duration, sometimes even when this has not been used previously in the experiment. Particularly good results are recorded if it is necessary to transfer from light signals, used for establishing a previous system of connections, to auditory signals (or conversely, if the previous system of connections was established to auditory signals).

Such differences are explained by saying that the inert verbal formulation, established in the formation of the previous connection and more closely connected with the signal used earlier, is somehow put into a compartment and this proceeds more easily the greater the difference between the new signal and the old.

These experiments have substantial significance for the analysis of the use of simple visual auxiliary aids in the training of child-oligophrenics (e.g. the use of tables with representations of objects during the instruction of children in arithmetical operations).

It is obvious that the use of different methods and shifts from one to another (particularly in a transference from the mastery of one operation or action to another) can raise the effectiveness of the adoption of a new method or action to a certain extent. More generally speaking, once we have learned that inertness is one of the most substantial pathological characteristics of higher nervous functioning in child-oligophrenics, we ought to create external conditions which facilitate transfers from the formation of one connection to another and transposition of connections. This is one of the conditions under which inertness can be overcome. Another condition is that in which there is special practice for the children in the establishment of their ability to make quick transfers of the meaning of signals and this gives them an opportunity to anticipate the formation of pathologically inert stereotypes. It was established in laboratory experiments that even in those cases where the child does not offer a correct verbal formulation of the transferring system of connections, verbally repeated transfers proceed more rapidly.

The question now arises as to whether the methods indicated here for the acceleration of the production of complex connections in child-oligophrenics and for the improvement in the realization and verbal expression of these connections are necessary. Perhaps the simple explanation of what it is necessary to do on the appearance of certain signals is sufficient for achieving these goals.

This question is forced upon us because in life and in school work the majority of new temporary connections are formed on the basis of explanations i.e. verbal instructions received from adults. This makes it necessary to study the formation in children of conditioned connections in accordance with verbal instruction and to compare this way of forming connections with their formation on the basis of speech reinforcement. We have examined this latter type of formation above.

All of the systems of connections described in this chapter are formed immediately in the normal child of 8 or 9 by verbal instruction. After a single explanation the child can repeat the instruction correctly, while conditioned responses and differentiation are established in the course of the initial presentations of the corresponding signals and these are stable. The conditioned responses are not inhibited by particular external causes and the differentiations are not prone to disinhibition. In this way in the formation of connections according to instructions the process of establishment is reduced—the connection appears immediately as if in a ready form. The actions of the child completely concord with the parameters given in the instruction while the verbal report corresponds to the actions and the instruction. All these three aspects of the formation of the connections are found in complete concordance.

In some child-oligophrenics (usually the older ones) an easy and quick formation of conditioned responses to a verbal instruction can be observed, but in the majority of children, especially the pupils in the junior classes of a special school (8–11 years old), it is quite otherwise. Even the act of remembering the instruction presents these children with considerable difficulties when a relatively complex system of connections is formulated in the instruction (e.g. when the following instruction is given, "Press when the red light comes on and immediately goes out, but when it stays on a long time, do not press!"). The child-oligophrenic often cannot even simply repeat such an instruction correctly and for him to achieve this, it must be repeated several times.

However, while normal children who can repeat correctly the instructions used in experiments always execute them correctly, child-oligophrenics of the same age do not always act correctly in response to presented signals even after achieving an exact repetition of the instruction. Frequently children do not give correct responses and differentiations, but more often they begin to act correctly and then the differentiations become disinhibited and the responses to certain conditioned signals drop out.

The instruction does not take away the influence of the old inert connections which frequently continue to appear after a new instruction has been given and disrupt its execution.

In this way the effect of the verbal explanation (the instruction) is extremely unstable and differentiation and positive conditioned responses are much less persistent (when they are being formed according to an instruction) than when they are formed with a preliminary instruction, but on the basis of speech reinforcement.* Continuous speech reinforcement results in a heightened level of excitation and in a concentration of nervous processes that facilitates the fixation of connections and increases their stability. From this it is clear that during the formation of relatively complex connections in child-oligophrenics it is expedient to apply continuous reinforcement on the one hand, and on the other hand it is expedient to use means, other than verbal explanation, to facilitate and accelerate the establishment of conditioned responses and differentiations. The application of these methods during the formation of conditioned responses according to instructions results in these connections being formed more quickly, being

* Investigations comparing the formation of conditioned connections in normal pre-school children 3–4 years old under conditions of speech reinforcement or verbal instruction, showed that the former conditions were more effective. (N. P. Paramonova.)

more stable and less subject to the influence of the pathological inertness of the old stereotypes.

The pathological inertness of the old stable verbal connection is one of the most significant pathological peculiarities in the neuro-dynamics of child-oligophrenics. It disrupts the formation of complex differentiations as we have seen above. However, there are other disturbances in the dynamics of the nervous processes which hinder the formation of complex temporary connections in oligophrenics. Among these, the weakness of differential inhibition in child-oligophrenics must be mentioned first.

As we have just said the weakness of differential inhibition is revealed with particular clarity when the complex differentiations described above are being formed according to preliminary verbal instruction.

It has been established in a series of studies that other forms of active inhibition are also weakened in child-oligophrenics. Significant disturbances in their formation of conditioned inhibition have been discovered. Conditioned inhibition is formed in the following way: another stimulus is added to the positive conditioned signal—this stimulus begins 2–3 seconds before the positive signal, is continued for the total duration of the positive signal and finishes with it. In contradistinction to the individually presented conditioned signal, the combination is reinforced negatively and consequently the conjunction of the additional stimulus—the conditioned inhibitor—signals that there ought to be no response to the conditioned signal and that it is necessary to inhibit the response.

The formation of a conditioned inhibitor is very difficult for child-oligophrenics and usually the formation of a conditioned inhibitor is replaced by the formation of a second order conditioned reflex: the children give a conditioned response when the additional stimulus appears.

The formation of delayed inhibition is even more difficult with child-oligophrenics. In the formation of this form of inhibition the reinforcement (in the formation of connections by the method of conditioned motor reflexes the verbal order "Press!" constitutes the reinforcement) is displaced to the end of the action of the conditioned signal, which in its own turn acts for a longer time.

Under normal conditions this displacement of the reinforcement to the end of the stimulus results in a response to the signal being displaced and delayed. As has been shown in recently conducted investigations, the formation of delayed inhibition is most difficult for healthy children and adults in comparison with other forms of internal inhibition. The delay of the response is possible for child-oligophrenics only when there is a very insignificant time interval. Subsequently the success in obtaining the former responses with a delay of 1·5–2 seconds shows that these are unique and that child-oligophrenics give precocious responses to many signals. This fact, like the retarded establishment of a delay, also indicates the weakness of active inhibition in child-oligophrenics.

The weakness of inhibition in these children is also revealed in the slow extinction of conditioned responses. The inhibition of conditioned responses to a conditioned stimulus is called extinction when the stimulus ceases to receive positive, and begins to receive negative, reinforcement (e.g. in the application of the method of conditioned motor responses with speech reinforcement, the response begins to be reinforced by the words "Don't press!"). The extinction of conditioned responses is particularly sharply delayed to stimuli in those systems of connections where the child cannot give a correct verbal account, i.e. those connections formed with an inadequate participation of the second signalling system.

Substantial disturbances in higher nervous functioning are revealed by child-oligophrenics during the establishment of conditioned reactions and differentiation to complex stimuli. A complex stimulus consisting of several simple signals, e.g. red, yellow, blue and green light signals (a four member complex) can become the excitatory basis of a conditioned response just as a simple stimulus can.*

* A complex in which the individual constituent stimuli follow one after the other, i.e. are distributed in time, is termed successive. If the individual components of a complex stimulus are presented together the complex stimulus is called a simultaneous complex.

The results of investigations have shown that a conditioned response is formed as easily to a successive complex as it is to a single complete stimulus in the normal child of school age. This is shown by the fact that the conditioned response arises in the form of a single press at the end of the complex and does not arise in response to the presentation of its individual components severally.

This obtains because of the synthesizing activity of the cortex and because of the unification into a single system of the excitation in the cortex arising from all the elements of the complex.

In child-oligophrenics the establishment of this reaction is difficult. These children usually give responses to each individual component of the complex. This attests to a disturbance in the synthesis of the individual elements into a single complex. The disturbance in the synthesis of the elements of a complex renders the establishment of a differentiation of complex stimuli impossible. These children cannot differentiate one complex (a chain of stimuli) from another which, for example, is distinguished from the first by a change in the position (transposition) of its middle members.

Disturbance in the synthesizing activity of the cortex in child-oligophrenics is revealed in the difficulty of the formation of two systems of connections simultaneously. For example, if a child-oligophrenic has established a conditioned response to a green light and a differentiation to a blue light and afterwards begins to form a new conditioned response to a yellow light, then when this is established, the conditioned response to the green light will be inhibited. If the response to the green light is re-established the conditioned reflex to the yellow light signal will be inhibited.

These phenomena show the difficulty of simultaneous co-existence, i.e. the synthesis of two connections, and they are probably associated with the pathological strengthening of negative induction in oligophrenics which has been observed in a series of studies.

Strong negative induction frequently leads to the child-oligophrenic experiencing great difficulties in school lessons where he has to perform certain actions in response to a whole system of instructions. He only reacts to some of these instructions and to individual stimuli. He ignores the rest. Under these circumstances the actions of the child sometimes completely lose their sense.

That strengthened negative induction is a characteristic feature of the higher nervous activity of child-oligophrenics and has great significance for the organization of their training.

3. Peculiarities of the Higher Nervous Activity of Child-oligophrenics of Various Clinical Groups

The peculiarities of higher nervous functioning described in the preceding section are common to all child-oligophrenics of junior school age. However, among the oligophrenics training in the special schools, several groups can be delineated according to the peculiarities of their behaviour and scholastic functioning. These groups are sharply distinguished one from another. The basic features of the clinico-psychological separation of child-oligophrenics according to different variants of defect were laid out in the Chapter 2. Here we will briefly examine the peculiarities in the higher nervous activity of the three basic clinical groups of oligophrenics:

(1) Those with well-balanced relations in the basic nervous processes.

(2) Those in whom the excitatory process definitely predominates.

(3) Those in whom inhibition predominates.

These groups have nothing in common with the types of higher nervous activity which is observed in normal children. All the three types of relationship between excitation and inhibition observed in children of these groups manifest themselves against a background of weakness in active internal inhibition, a sharply pronounced inertness of the nervous processes and a weakness of the synthesizing functioning of the cortex.

Among the child-oligophrenics training in the special schools a rather large group is comprised of children with an absence of a pronounced dominance of excitation or inhibition. For the sake of brevity we will call the child-oligophrenics of this group, the first group. Positive conditioned connections are more easily established and become stable somewhat more quickly in the first than in the other groups—although this first group is slower than normal children. The faster stabilization of conditioned connections shows that the excitatory process is faster and better concentrated in this group than in other oligophrenic groups. This is also shown by their better expression of the stabilization of conditioned responses and the small quantity of inter-signal responses, which are, however, totally absent in normal school children of the same age.

When new stimuli are introduced after the formation of the first positive conditioned connection, the children of this group give generalized responses to all stimuli impinging on the same analyser as the positive signal. For example, after the establishment of a conditioned response to a light signal the most diverse light signals used for the first time in these experimental conditions can immediately evoke motor responses.

In some cases responses which have not been conditioned arise to various stimuli impinging on other analysers.

Stimulus generalization is much narrower in children of the first group than in those of the excitable group but is wider than in normal school children in whom only similar stimuli to the positive conditioned signal exhibit generalization. The characteristics of the generalization to freshly introduced stimuli are also defined by the character of the irradiation of excitation which is considerably narrower in the first group than it is for instance in excitable oligophrenics. It is broader than normal, however.

The external inhibition of established conditioned connections evoked by strong super-stimuli (new stimuli occurring suddenly) is pronounced in child-oligophrenics of the first group. It is stronger than in normal school children, but much weaker than in child-oligophrenics of the other groups. Usually the inhibition of conditioned responses or the disinhibition of a differentiation is observed only within the limit of the one signal succeeding the super-stimulus. Often the inhibition is only expressed as a change in the latency or magnitude of a response.

Differentiations are formed more quickly in children of this group than in excitable children, but somewhat more slowly (on average) than in inhibitory oligophrenics and normal children of the same age.

The transfer of the conditioned meaning of stimuli occurs comparatively quickly in the first group and the change of inhibitory significance to positive and positive to inhibitory proceeds more or less similarly.

As in the other child-oligophrenics, in children of the first group the most serious deviations from the norm and the greatest disturbances are observed during the establishment of complex connections (serious disturbances in the verbal account, the inertness of connections previously established, the delayed formation of complex differentiations).

Simple conditioned connections according to verbal instruction are formed quickly and stably in these children. However, disturbances which are not encountered in pupils of ordinary schools are observed during the formation of more complex connections in accordance with verbal instruction.

Children in whom excitation is predominant form a second group of child-oligophrenics.

With them simple positive conditioned connections are established quickly, but in many cases they become stable slowly. However, in some children with a particularly pronounced predominance of excitation it is just not possible to achieve stable conditioned responses. Conditioned responses in such children are camouflaged by frequent inter-signal responses. The stabilization of conditioned responses is sharply disturbed—over a series of several experiments all responses remain unequal in vigour, duration and latency. The generalization of the positive signal to new stimuli is extremely diffuse in this group and extends far beyond the bounds of the group of stimuli to which the positive conditioned signal belongs. For example, after a first conditioned response has been established to a green light signal, immediately on the initial presentation all light signals and also various sound stimuli will also evoke the same conditioned response. All these facts testify to the strongly expressed and widely extensive irradiation of excitation.

The external inhibition exhibited by this group is much stronger than in oligophrenics of the first group: this is particularly evident in the disinhibition of differentiation by super-stimuli. The formation of simple differentiation is usually somewhat delayed in this group, while complex differentiation (of the type where differentiation is according to the duration of the stimuli) is just not established or is established with great difficulty and is unstable. Not infrequently even simple differentiation is disinhibited. It is in these peculiarities that the sharply pronounced weakness of the internal inhibition in excitable children is revealed.

The specific peculiarities of this group are also manifested in the transfer of the conditioned significance of stimuli: when a previously inhibitory signal begins to be reinforced positively, it acquires its new significance several times faster than a previously positive signal becomes inhibitory and differentiated. In addition these children often give responses to the new signal differentiated as a result of the transfer although these are weak and slightly inhibited, i.e. the differentiation following the transfer often remains incomplete.

In the verbal accounts of these children a large number of collateral connections and the serious inertness of speech stereotypes formed earlier can be observed. The formation of conditioned connections according to verbal instruction is sharply disturbed. Even simple differentiation formed according to instructions is unstable, while these are formed with great difficulty in some children.

Thus in child-oligophrenics of the second group there is a significant predominance of the excitatory process and this is associated with the very strongly pronounced weakness of internal inhibition. The process of excitation arises and irradiates widely in the cerebral cortex.

The pathological inertness of the nervous process is very strongly expressed both in the form of an inertness of positive conditioned connections formed earlier and in more elementary manifestations (repetitive responses of a perseverative type and the tonicity of conditioned responses).

Children with a predominance of inhibition constitute the third important group of oligophrenic pupils in the special schools.

In them the tonicity of motor responses is manifested for a particularly long time. Along with this, in the presence of this overt form of inertness in the motor analyser, the inertness in the form of movements of a perseverative nature, which was strongly expressed in the first and second groups, is almost absent in this group. Perseverative movements are easily inhibited and do not re-appear after several negative reinforcements. Inter-signal responses are rarely observed. The speed of the formation of conditioned responses is somewhat slower, their stability is delayed and their stabilization is sharply disturbed. The magnitude of conditioned responses is reduced in comparison with other groups and the comparative latency increased.

A specific peculiarity of the established conditioned connections in children of the third group is the fact that after gaps in an experiment and particularly gaps between experiments, conditioned responses become inhibited and are restored only after the presentation of several signals or after the introduction of reinforcement.

In these children many new stimuli being used for the first time and affecting the same analyser as the positive signal, are generalized from the last signal—although the generalization is usually not observed immediately, but only after a repeated presentation of stimuli. As well as this, strong incidental stimuli evoke the inhibition of conditioned responses—sometimes for a long period.

Differentiations are formed somewhat more quickly in many children of this group than in other oligophrenics. The quick formation of differentiations in children of the third group is associated with the characteristics of the stimulus generalization in these children: as was noted above, these children cannot generalize from the conditioned signal on the first presentation of new stimuli, i.e. the conditioned motor response is not evoked. If the absence of the response is reinforced as being correct, then naturally the response does not develop to the new signal subsequently and it becomes differentiated. Thus in child-oligophrenics of the third group simple differentiations are formed "on the spot" without any process of development.

However, no significant differences are observed in the speed of the establishment of more complex differentiations in children of the "inhibitory" group and the well-balanced oligophrenics. The answers of inhibitory children to questions about the connections being formed are distinguished by several specific characteristics: they are usually extremely brief, monosyllabic, and there are usually long pauses between the question and answer—sometimes lasting half a minute or even longer. Not infrequently these children answer a question only after it has been repeated.

The pathological inertness of old verbal connections emerges clearly in the formation of complex connections. It is revealed to a considerably greater degree in children of this group than it is in children who have no sharp predominance of one of the basic nervous processes.

The transfer of the conditioned meaning of stimuli also has a distinctive feature in the inhibitory group: the inhibitory stimulus becomes positive slowly in the presence of appropriate reinforcement, while a positive signal becomes inhibitory more quickly than in other children. This is particularly evident in initial transfer trials.

The formation of complex connections according to verbal instruction is disturbed in this group of children almost as much as it is in excitable children. In this method of forming connections a large number of responses to conditioned signals are omitted in this group, while in some cases all conditioned responses are inhibited. Thus the low persistence of verbal instruction is extremely noticeable in inhibitory as well as excitable children.

From the characteristics enumerated it can be seen that the pathological predominance of inhibition in this group of children is associated with a sharp reduction of the amenability to excitation of the cortical cells. In the presence of a relative predominance of inhibition the absolute strength of the inhibitory process is low. As with excitable children, children with a predominance of inhibition exhibit pathologically strengthened irradiation. However, this is basically expressed in the strengthening of the irradiation of the inhibitory process. The pathological inertness of the nervous processes is very strong in children of the inhibitory group.

*   *

*

The peculiarities of higher nervous activity described here with reference to child-oligophrenics of junior school age change later on under the influence of training and development. It is important to note that these changes occur unequally in the different groups. They are relevant to only one parameter of higher nervous functioning while they occur within each group in relation to different parameters.

Thus the pathologically extending irradiation weakens and becomes more limited. This is expressed in an acceleration of the development of stability in conditioned connections and this changes particularly strongly in the excitable and inhibitory children approximating to what is observed in well-balanced children. It is expressed in an improvement in the stabilization of conditioned responses and in a restriction of the generalization from the positive signal to freshly introduced stimuli. While in younger children of the "excitable" group there is gross diffuse generalization, extending to the limits of the analyser, in older children the only freshly introduced stimuli which are generalized from a positive signal, are those directed to the same analyser as the conditioned signal. Stimulus generalization is sharply reduced in older children of the inhibitory group and extends only to stimuli similar to the positive signal.

Inter-signal responses completely disappear in older children of the well-balanced and inhibitory groups and are rarely seen even in excitable children.

With the increase in age of the children described there is a strengthening of internal inhibition manifested as a degree of acceleration in the establishment and in the development of stability of differentiation. Thus while complex differentiation is not established in excitable children of junior school age, it is in older children of this group, though more slowly than in older oligophrenics of other groups. Established differentiation in older children is much more persistent and not so easily disinhibited as in younger children.

Manifestations of external inhibition become more feeble and established conditioned connections are more stable in relation to incidental influences.

The inertness of nervous processes decreases with age. The tonicity of conditioned responses being newly-formed is reduced and superfluous movements of a perseverative character are more easily inhibited. The inertness of old, firmly established verbal stereotypes ceases to appear during the formation of simple conditioned connections and with complex connections it is of short duration.

With increasing age the formation of conditioned connections in accordance with verbal instruction improves considerably and this improvement is particularly evident in excitable and inhibitory children for whom, in many cases, the formation of such connections was unattainable when they were of junior school age.

All the changes described lead to some levelling out of the differences between the groups. However, specific features characteristic of higher nervous functioning of the children in each group, are preserved at a later age, just as the significant deviations in the higher nervous functioning of child-oligophrenics from that of their normal peers, is preserved. In particular the inertness of the nervous processes (especially in the form of the inertness of old firmly established verbal connections) continues to be a characteristic feature of the higher nervous activity of child-oligophrenics of all groups, in spite of all the convergence described above.

CHAPTER 6

THE ROLE OF SPEECH IN THE FORMATION OF TEMPORARY CONNECTIONS AND IN THE REGULATION OF THE BEHAVIOUR OF CHILD-OLIGOPHRENICS

1. *Basic Functions of Speech*

In this chapter we will examine the characteristics of higher nervous processes which arise with the development of speech and the changes which appear in the organization of human behaviour.

We will briefly compare the development of human behaviour with the process of the development of new experience in animals.

Natural science indicates two important factors fundamental to the development of the behaviour of animals. An animal receives part of the forms of its behaviour ready made, from previous generations; it inherits these forms from its ancestors. The bee does not learn to construct a honey-comb and the spider does not learn to spin a web. These "abilities" are inherited from previous generations in exactly the same way as the form of the wings and the structure of the eye are inherited. These inherited forms of behaviour constitute one section of an animal's behaviour and occupy a greater place the lower we descend down the evolutionary scale. The second section of behaviour is comprised of these aspects which the animal acquires during its life. Charles Darwin discovered the origin of instincts. I. P. Pavlov discovered the origin of new, individually developed forms of behaviour when he studied the mechanisms of the formation of conditioned reflexes. The higher the position an animal occupies on the evolutionary scale, the greater the role played by the forms of behaviour acquired in its individual experience.

The behaviour of man includes both these forms, but man possesses yet another means of acquiring new experience which animals do not.

No animal can acquire new knowledge or abilities except by direct interaction with the environment. There are no animals which can ask their elders how to perform a certain action. There are none to which the experience of previous generations can be transmitted by any means other than by direct heredity or direct imitation.

It is quite different with man. Man masters verbal speech and with its help he can assimilate experience accumulated over a thousand years of humanity's history.

When a child asks his mother, "What is that?" and the mother answers, "That is a steam engine" and then explains its construction, the child is absorbing something that has been achieved by the labours of many generations. When the school child learns reading and writting, arithmetic and basic science, he is acquiring the experience of all humanity: he could not master one millionth part of this, if the whole of his development was limited to the experience he obtains as a result of direct interaction with the environment. Because of speech communication a child acquires a new factor of development—the assimilation of experience common to all mankind, and this factor quickly becomes the basic factor forming his psyche.

The development of the mind by means of the acquisition through language of experience common to mankind is the third type of development. It does not exist in animals and is the grand acquisition of human society. For animals there is only evolution, but for man, history is more important and man's accumulated forms of behaviour must be examined as a product of his social history and not as a biological product.

The communicative function is the main function of human speech and without it the assimilation of the experience of former generations would be impossible. However, it would be incorrect to imagine that this exhausts the basic functions of speech.

Language is not only a means of communication: as well as this it is an instrument for thinking.

The child who has absorbed language has an opportunity to organize his perception and memory in a new way. He can master more complex forms of the aspects of environmental objects. He has the opportunity to draw conclusions from his observations, to make inferences, and to meditate.

When a child names a thing, saying "That is an ink-well", or, "That is a steam engine", he is simultaneously producing an analysis of it with the help of means brought together over many generations. (Transcribed, ink-well is "chernilitsa".) He discriminates the root "chern" (black) and thus refers the perceived thing to the group of other things concerned with colours. He discriminates the suffix "il" denoting the quality of instrumentality and he classifies "chernila" in the same group as the words "belila" (bleach) and "tochilo" (grindstone) etc. In discriminating the second suffix "nits", he indicates that the perceived object has the quality of a container and refers it to the same group of things as "sakar-nitsa-a" (sugar bowl) and "perech-nits-a" (pepper-pot). When he says "paravoz" (steam-engine) he begins to understand that steam (para) plays a role in the movement of the named machine and that this machine pulls (-voz) other objects. When he masters and uses words, the child analyses and synthesizes the manifestations of the external world and for this he uses the experience of humanity as well as his own personal experience. He classifies objects and he begins to see them in different ways as well as remembering them differently.

The speech which the child assimilates does not consist of individual words, but of complex grammatical combinations and whole expressions. These expressions enable the analysis and synthesis of perceptions, the connecting of things with actions, and in addition the placing of objects into known relationships with each other. When he acquires the forms of developed connected speech, the child acquires the ability to draw conclusions from accepted assumptions, to master the logic of connections and to come to know laws extending far beyond the limits of direct, personal experience. Finally he masters science and is able to foresee and predict events which he himself did not witness.

If we were to stop at this point we would not have fully elucidated the role of speech in the formation of human mental processes.

Speech activity is not only a means of communication and instrument of thinking, but is also a method of *regulating behaviour*.

When a mother says to her child, "That is a cup", the child turns his head and looks at the named object. When mother says to him "Clap!", he raises his hands and claps. The mother's remark regulates the child's behaviour.

However, the ability to regulate another's behaviour with the help of speech is only one aspect of this important function of speech. When a child subordinates himself to a verbal order of an adult, he assimilates this method of organizing actions. He himself begins to form the pattern of his own future actions. Speech reflects the connections and relationships of reality and formulates the modes of future action. Speech, addressed as an order to oneself, quickly becomes one of the most important methods of regulating behaviour in the development of the child. Wherever man performs voluntary acts, which apparently have no cause and thereby apparently violate a universal natural law, then overt or covert (internal) speech always lies at the basis of these actions, in accordance with the law that every event must have a cause. Speech revives traces of past experience, the signals of which are those real signals which, like all others, are only signals but are incomparably more generalized and labile. The direction of his behaviour with the help of these signals is what basically distinguishes the mental activity of man from the behaviour of animals.

The question arises now as to what part speech plays in the acquisition of new experience in the normal and the mentally retarded child.

In all this the behaviour of the young child is fundamentally different from that of the school child. The latter analyses the

conditions of an experiment earlier and formulates a rule of behaviour before he begins to put any action into practice. The former
forms a motor habit and cannot then say anything about it.

We can say that the formation of a conditioned motor reaction
(motor habit) in the child of three rarely proceeds with the full
participation of his speech. The speech does not emerge here as
a means of orientation in the experimental conditions, nor as a
method of formulating a rule or the structure of the appropriate
behaviour. The ability to utilize speech as a means of communicating with others has been adequately consolidated, but it is inadequately applied as a means of orientation in a situation and as a
means of regulating his behaviour.

It is only somewhat later when the child is 3·5–4 that the picture
changes substantially. The child who receives the order, "Press!"
after the flashing of the red light, does not subsequently anticipate
this order. When the light comes on the next time the child immediately addresses the experimenter, "It is necessary to press now?"
When he has received the negative order, "Don't press!" he does
not cease to press all subsequent signals and he again asks the
experimenter, "Is it necessary now?" This shows the absence of
his assimilation of the evaluation of the signal significance of the
light flashing on and he addresses the adult in order to obtain from
him the rule which should define subsequent reactions. The child
of this age embraces speech as a mode of communication in order
to widen the information at his disposal by this means and to
formulate the required rule of behaviour.

This stage is, however, not final and if the child of 3·5–4 does
not obtain a prepared answer from the adult, after several attempts
he formulates the rule himself, and says, "It means when there
is a red light it is necessary to press!" From being a mode of communication his speech changes here into an instrument of generalization, with the inference of a rule. The rule inferred by
the child sharply changes the course of the further formation of
a habit.

This problem was partially broached in the last chapter and is
one of the most important. We must stop and consider it.

2. *The Role of Speech in the Production of New Connections in the Normal and Mentally Retarded Child*

We will dwell briefly on the formation of all three of the just mentioned functions of speech in the child and their manner of insuring the most complex task of speech—the regulation of the child's voluntary behaviour.

Even from a very early age the child begins to assimilate the speech addressed to him: at first the general tone, then individual words and finally complex combinations containing these and information an adult addresses to the child. In the early stages of development information is received by the child only in those cases where the speech of the adult is contained in syntax intelligible to the child. It suffices to say something to the child towards the end of tth first year of his life in an unusual tone, in an unusual situation, or under circumstances where the speech is not accompanied by concrete action, to see that the content of the speech remains incomprehensible to the child. It is only at the end of the third year of life that the child begins to understand phrases of relatively complex structure.

A similar complex course is followed by the child's ability to perform a speech instruction of an adult. Even towards the end of the first year of life the child is able to execute simple orders from an adult. However, he can only execute these when the order is uttered in a familiar (and most often in a sufficiently emotional) tone and is given in a familiar situation. An order which is given in an unfamiliar tone or situation is not executed by the child. For example, if a child beginning his second year has to pick up a doll, while a cockerel lies in the way to the doll, the child will not be able to execute the adult's speech instruction. When he stretches towards the doll, he will pick up the cockered lying on the way to it. If a child of this age is asked to *take off* a wheel which he is putting on an axle, the speech instruction of the adult, which clashes with the action already performed, proves beyond accomplishment and the child, on hearing the instruction, begins to perform the first action more intensively.

Speech communicating some content or order can be understood by the child but in the first stages the effect of the speech order is easily disrupted if the content comes into conflict with the situation directly influencing the child.

It is only much later, towards three or three and a half, that the comprehension of the speech of an adult and the execution of tasks formulated in speech become formed to such an extent that speech is able to define the further activity of the child independently of the conditions in which it is uttered.

Does this mean, however, that the generalizing functions of speech are, to a considerable extent, stored up until this age? Does this mean that the child who has reached this stage of development can independently utilize his speech so as to regulate his behaviour?

We will try to answer these questions with the help of special observations.

We may conduct these experiments (which were reported in the previous chapter) with a child of 2–2·5 years. We present some signals to the child (for example, the flashing of a red light), accompanying each of these signals with the verbal order, "Press the button!" and we give him other signals (for example, the flashing of a green light) accompanying each of these with the order, "Don't press!".

Does the child of $2\frac{1}{2}$ to 3 assimilate this simple rule formulated as an order? Can he generalize to the simple general rule, "It is necessary to press the button every time a red light flashes and to withhold a press whenever a green light flashes." Is the production of the conditioned motor response firmly mediated by such a rule formulated in speech?

In the conducting of this experiment (such experiments were performed by N.P. Paramonova and O.K. Tikhomirov) the picture which can be observed sharply differentiates children of this age from older children. At first the child presses the button only in response to a direct verbal order. A conditioned motor response to the red light is not formed at all to start with. The exact combination of the red light and the order, "Press!" has to be repeated many times for the child to begin to press the button on the appearance of the light alone.

This conditioned reflex initially has an undifferentiated character and the presentation of any light—yellow, blue, or green—evokes the same reaction from the child. However, if the appearance of a green light is accompanied by the order, "Do not press!" once, the child ceases to press the button in response to all the other signals including the red one. It is necessary to proceed for a long time with the child for the conditioned response to gradually acquire a more precise and differentiated form. The presentation of the red light begins to evoke a fast motor response from the child only gradually, while the presentation of the green light, which initially evoked a slow and weak movement, completely ceases to evoke a motor response. In this instance, however, the differential conditioned reaction of the child cannot be considered to be stably laid down and it is only necessary for the experimenter to cease saying, "Correct" after every movement of the child (or after his withholding of the response) for the child to stop giving the required reactions. When he does not receive the necessary evaluation of his action the child again begins either to press each successive signal or to refrain from pressing altogether. A small pause in the experiments or a suddenly developing incidental stimulus can have the same effect.

The uniqueness of this continually developing conditioned reaction in the young child appears in yet another important characteristic. If we ask the child to recount how he reacts to the presented stimuli, we immediately see a series of peculiarities which distinguish his behaviour in a fundamental way from the behaviour of an older child, school child, or adult. It emerges that even after the motor habits—to press the button on the appearance of the red light and not to press when the green appears—have been formed in the young child, he is quite unable to formulate verbally the rule which he is in fact following. When asked by the experimenter what he has just seen, the child may answer, "Mama". To the question, "What were you doing?", he may answer "I was walking." Even when the question refers directly to the connection which has just been formed and the child is asked point-blank, "When did you press?", the perplexed child either just cannot answer the question or he replies "Just now!"

When he has formulated the rule, the child mediates all his subsequent behaviour with it. "Now I must press!" he says, as soon as the red light comes on. "It is not necessary now," he says when the green light comes on. The selective reaction necessary according to the experimental conditions begins to be formed quickly, sometimes immediately, in a flash. This quick and immediately insightful formation of a motor reaction is a sure sign that the movements of the child have ceased to be mechanical and have become conscious on the basis of the mediation of speech.

The transition to the conscious formation of habits marks a most important stage in the behaviour of the child. It is revealed not only in the fact that the child's habits begin to form incomparably faster, but that these habits immediately acquire a considerably greater stability. Now the formulated system of reactions is not extinguished when the experimenter ceases to reinforce the child reactions with the word "Correct". This is not necessary now for the child since the process of the formation of the habit based on a formulated rule becomes a self-regulatory process, receiving its reinforcement from the coincidence of his reactions with the rule.

While earlier each correct action of the child was reinforced by the approval of an adult, now the coincidence of the reaction with the verbally formulated rule is the reinforcement of his responses and just because of this, the correct mode of reacting becomes stable. Now a short pause or an incidental stimulus does not lead to a disruption of the system formed. The child remembers the rule and steadily maintains the mode of behaviour he has acquired. Now when the child is asked by us what he has done and just when does he press the button, he formulates the rule from the start, "When it is red, I press. When it is green, I don't", and this reply about his actions shows us that we have here conscious and specifically human behaviour.

We have elucidated briefly the complex processes of the formation of conscious behaviour in the child's early stages of development and we can now turn directly to the problem which concerns us in the book.

Experiments conducted with mentally retarded children show how sharply different in them is the participation of speech in the formation of new connections from what we see when we analyse the process in normal children.

We saw above that it was only in the most simple cases when, for instance, a red light is accompanied by the order "Press!", while the green is accompanied by the order "Don't press!", that the mentally retarded child grasps what he has to do and formulates the necessary rule. However, this task is too simple for the child of 8 or 9 (and sometimes 10 to 12) and as an example it tells us nothing sufficiently clearly about the role which speech in fact plays in the child's orientation to the external world and the organization of his behaviour. It is sufficient to complicate the task somewhat for the real state of affairs to emerge with much greater clarity.

We may present the mentally retarded child with a task whose solution requires some preliminary analysis of the presented stimuli. For instance, (as we have already shown above) we may accompany each *long* signal of a blue light with the order "Press!" and each *short* signal of the same colour with the order "Don't press!". In this case for the correct solution of the problem the child must make a preliminary analysis of the signal: he is not to pay attention to their identical colour, but has to separate out their differing feature—duration. He must formulate a general rule on the basis of the abstraction conducted.

Experiments performed have enabled us to uncover the features which characterize the mentally retarded child.

In general a child with a severe degree of mental retardation solves this problem without any rule. Usually he presses the button for all blue signals. He does not notice how they differ and does not connect the differential reinforcements ("Press!" or "Don't press!") with the duration of the signal. Frequently he generalizes the order and ceases to press to all signals, subsequent to one of them being accompanied by the order "Don't press!", or he begins to press to all signals when another is accompanied by the order "Press!" Only after many failures does he begin to address the experimenter with the question, "Is it necessary to press now?" He does not draw any conclusions from the answer received and when the next signal appears he again asks in a stereotyped way, "Is it necessary to press now?" However, the significance of the questions he puts is not to obtain the necessary data for an independent formulation of a rule, but is to save him from thinking about the rule, to avoid any tension, and to act every time according to a prepared order.

While the question to the adult is only a step towards an independent conclusion for the normal child, it is a way of escaping from a task requiring some thought for the child with a severe form of mental retardation.

The uses of speech by the child with a less pronounced degree of mental retardation are similar to this. Feeble-minded children also ask the experimenter, "Is it necessary to press now?" while these questions also do not lead to independent thinking and the answers obtained are not used to formulate the necessary rule independently. The basic difference in these children from those just described is that they try to draw the necessary conclusion from the questions addressed to the adult and the answers. However, their conclusions are not sufficiently generalized and while responding correctly to the next signal, they continue to ask, "Is it necessary to press now?" Even when they receive confirmation of the correctness of their solution, they do not cease to put questions subsequently and they do not formulate the general rule which would render these questions superfluous.

The inability to make use of knowledge obtained in the course of speech communication, the inability to assimilate speech instructions in a generalized form, and the inability to use speech as a means of independent thinking, are characteristic of mentally retarded feeble-minded children. Evidently these features constitute one of their basic characteristics.

The inability to transfer to an independent speech analysis

of a presented problem and to an independent formulation of a rule of action results in the participation of speech in the production of new connections in child-oligophrenics being considerably limited.

The child-oligophrenic can easily state in speech those signs which he perceives visually, but he is unable to discriminate the relatively weaker signs and fixate their significance as signals with the help of speech. In other words he is unable to produce any complex analysis or synthesis which would lead to an exact rule of reacting. Consequently in complicated conditions these children respond with a press on the button only on the direct order of the experimenter for a long time, and it is only gradually and after many combinations of the order and the presented stimulus that they begin to establish a temporary connection.

For these very reasons the establishment of temporary connections in child-oligophrenics differs in a fundamental way from their establishment in normal children. With the latter there is a rule to which the actions of the child must be subordinated, it is cognized from the start and the connection is formed quickly and is immediately stable. With child-oligophrenics the rule is established mechanically, step by step. For a long time it continues to be insufficiently stable and most important it is not formulated in the speech of such a child and it is not cognized by him. Sometimes it is sufficient to make a small break or to introduce a strong incidental stimulus in the experiment for the forming connection to be disrupted. It is sufficient for the experimenter to cease to say, "Correct" to the child every time and to leave it for him to say it to himself for the system of reactions, which the child was developing in the familiar conditions, to be destroyed: he will once more begin to respond randomly.

The habit remains unstable for a long time in the initial stages of this mechanical development. After very great and prolonged training, during which every signal is always accompanied by the order, "Press!" or "Don't press!" the habit becomes sufficiently stable. However, as well as this it becomes very inert and sluggish and if we attempt to reverse this habit (for example, accompanying each short signal with the order, "Press!" and each long one with the order "Don't press!") we see that the child reacts to the signal presentations as before, in spite of the verbal instruction. He persistently produces the system of responses learned or, if the orders which are inconsistent with the established habit continue, he completely loses whatever system he had and begins to respond only in accordance with the orders of the experimenter.

The experienced teacher will easily see a familiar picture in this fact. It is difficult to establish any habit in such a pupil and it is extremely sluggish when it has to be changed.

The difficulty and slowness of the consolidation of new connections in those cases where the problem posed is relatively complex and the sluggishness and inertness of an established habit are two features which characterize the establishment of complex connections in the mentally retarded child and lie at the root of the peculiarities of his training so well known to the pedagogue.

3. *The Regulation of Actions by Speech in the Normal and Mentally Retarded Child*

In order to understand more easily the conditions under which speech can accomplish its regulatory role we will examine the process of composition of this regulatory function in the early stages of the development of the normal child.

We have said that the child of $1-1\frac{1}{2}$ years of age can already execute an order spoken by an adult successfully and that the speech perceived by him begins to play its regulatory role here. However, we know that the regulatory function of an adult's order is far from being conserved under all conditions.

The same picture can be observed in the child of $2-2\frac{1}{2}$, if the most simple of those experiments described above are conducted with him.

Let us put a rubber bulb in the child's hand and tell him to press it as soon as a red light flashes in front of him. It would seem that he ought to perform this task easily. The child understands the instruction and can even recall it if asked to do so. However, when the rubber bulb is put in his hand, he presses it without waiting for the signal. When the red light flashes on he begins to examine it, temporarily forgetting about the task which he has to perform.

The integration of speech and action is difficult for him and the perceived spoken instruction does not lead to the performance of the necessary task. The child may either listen to the instruction and repeat it or immediately respond to the object he sees. Naturally in these circumstances instruction by speech from the adult cannot play its necessary regulatory role.

In other instances the child assimilates the instruction as a synthetic whole and in the most simple instances he begins to execute them. In response to the flashing on of the red light the child can follow the instruction received and press the rubber bulb. However, his presses do not cease when the light is extinguished. The processes of excitation evoked by the signal are so diffuse that the child continues to press the bulb and is unable to inhibit these movements. The speech of an adult is unable to stop excitation which has begun to be aroused. Even if we say to the child, "When the light is no longer there, don't press!", he is unable to execute the order. Sometimes the order, "Don't go on pressing!" can even evoke the opposite effect and only intensifies the presses on the rubber bulb. In this case the speech of the adult acts *non-specifically* on the child. It only serves to start actions, but cannot inhibit them.

All these conditions—the difficulty in the synthesis of speech instruction and action, the great diffusiveness of the child's nervous processes, the unstable and specific effect of speech—are important obstacles preventing the spoken instruction of an adult from acquiring its real regulatory role.

This weakness of the regulatory role of speech can be observed in a child between 3 and $3\frac{1}{2}$.

If we switch on first a red and then a green light in front of a child of this age and tell him to press the bulb in response to the red, but not to press in response to the green, we will notice that he cannot in fact perform this task even although he has understood the instruction. The process of excitation which is at the basis of his movements is so diffuse at this age and the process of inhibition so weak, that once the child has started to press the bulb in response to the appearance of the red light, he impulsively presses it upon the appearance of a blue light although he remembers the instruction clearly. The regulatory role of speech here is too weak to overcome the diffuseness of the process of excitation, while the connection of the instruction with the movement is so inadequate that the child often cannot even notice his mistakes and will believe that he has performed the required task accurately.

Is it possible to consolidate the regulatory role of spoken instruction in these instances and still achieve a correct performance from the child?

Experiments show the best ways of finding this out. The simplest way is a frequent repetition of the instruction in contiguity with the given signal. If each signal is accompanied by a verbal order, with the order, "Press!" being repeated after the red light, and, "Don't press!", after the green, then concentration of the nervous processes is consolidated and the child retains the instruction given to him and is now able to execute it successfully.

However, it is possible to find another, more rational method of overcoming the initial diffuseness of the nervous processes and of consolidating the regulatory role of verbal instruction. For this we can turn to the speech of the child himself, which by this age is reaching a level at which it is beginning to possess certain attributes essential for becoming a regulator of behaviour.

We will attempt to change our experiment somewhat. We will ask the child of 3–3½ (as did O. K. Tikhomirov) not to press when the red signal appears, but only to respond to it with the word, "Necessary!" In response to the green signal he is to say another word, "Unnecessary!" The results of this experiment show that a child who is unable to respond to both signals with different *movements*, can respond successfully with different *words*: he does not make a mistake saying, "Necessary!" on one occasion and, "Unnecessary!" on another. These verbal responses reveal *greater lability* and *greater control* than motor responses. Thus when we cannot master the child's movements, we can master his speech.

Can't we exploit this characteristic of the already developed speech of the child and make it a means of controlling his movements? Can't we avoid repeating the appropriate order every time and get the child himself to do it for us and by this method use his own speech for the regulation of his motor acts?

Experiments show that this is quite possible. If we first ask the child to dictate to himself, "Necessary!" when the red signal appears simultaneously pressing the rubber bulb, we notice that his own speech strengthens the effect of the instruction and will regulate his motor responses successfully. However, this is only possible when the child *is silent* while the green light appears. If we ask him to say loudly, "Unnecessary!", as well as "Necessary!", pressing in one case and withholding the press in the other, then the task proves to be too difficult for him.

The excitation aroused by the loud pronunciation of the word, "Unnecessary!" is so great that it overcomes the inhibitory effect of the word's meaning. When the child says, "Unnecessary!", loudly, he simultaneously presses the bulb strongly, only subsequently noticing that he has violated the instruction.

It is only towards $4\frac{1}{2}$ to 5 that the direct (or as is sometimes said "impulsive") influence of the speech response weakens and is replaced by the stronger influence of the connections of meaning lying behind the word. Then the speech of the child begins to regulate his motor responses successfully. Later on the speech of this child becomes a sufficiently strong regulatory factor for him to begin to perform tasks without any external talking.

What is the situation regarding the regulatory function of speech in mentally retarded children?

In the experiments we have described in detail above, it was noted that the mentally retarded child achieves an understanding of the sequence of the motor responses required of him and can formulate the necessary rule, only as a result of protracted practice. However, in spite of this, his motor responses remain incorrect and the assimilated rule does not regulate their flow in the necessary way.

What lies at the root of this disturbance of the regulatory role of speech in the child-oligophrenic in such instances?

As we saw in the previous chapter, the dynamics of the nervous processes in the mentally retarded child are sharply disturbed. The tonus of the basic nervous processes (especially inhibition) is weakened and the nervous processes concentrate with difficulty; every incidental influence easily inhibits an initiated response. In these conditions the creation of the systems of excitation necessary for every motor act to be mediated by speech is made very difficult. Because of this difficulty attempts of the child to turn to his own speech for regulating his motor processes are often unsuccessful. The child begins to dictate the necessary action to himself, but the act proves so difficult for him that it attracts all his attention and it inhibits all other motor acts. He begins to press the rubber bulb, but then the effect of his speech command is inhibited and the system disintegrates.

The investigations of E. D. Khomskaya and E. N. Myrtsinovskaya have shown that the difficulty of creating a unitory dynamic speech-motor system is an important physiological factor preventing the mentally retarded child from performing a complex action.

Yet another factor is fundamental to the difficulty of the mentally retarded child in the regulating of his own actions. As we have already said above, the child's own speech can regulate his motor processes only when the nervous processes basic to speech are greater in their susceptibility to concentration and their lability than the nervous processes fundamental to the motor responses. However, the speech connections of the child-oligophrenic are not more, but less, labile than his motor responses and they more easily change into fixed stereotypes.

We will only give two examples illustrating this situation.

A child-oligophrenic has to respond to a red signal with a press, but has to refrain from pressing to a green signal. For some time he executes this instruction sufficiently well. Subsequently the experimental conditions are changed and the child has to respond to the red signal with the word, "Necessary", and to the green signal with the word, "Unnecessary".

When he is performing this task the child frequently loses the correct sequence of responses very quickly and monotonously alternates his responses, "Necessary"—"Unnecessary", independently of the signals. Sometimes he sticks to one of these responses and repeats it the whole time, "Unnecessary" ... "Unnecessary", or he produces one and the same speech stereotype without any signal.

In all these cases the nervous processes fundamental to speech are so inert that the speech responses themselves easily lose their meaning and their correct character. The speech processes of the child-oligophrenic change very easily into inert stereotypes and this is the real reason why they cannot play their necessary role in the regulation of actions.

*   *

*

We have completed our survey and can give a brief resumé of the way in which the higher nervous processes of the mentally retarded child are distinguished from the processes of the higher nervous activity of his normal peer.

The more complex forms of higher nervous activity of the normal child are developed in the course of communication with adults. In the process of this communication speech is assimilated and very rapidly becomes the instrument of thinking and a means of regulating behaviour. We may say that no single behavioural act is formed in the normal child without the participation of speech which systematizes his past experience and directs his active behaviour.

It is quite otherwise with the mentally retarded child. In the course of his development he also masters speech, but the nervous processes fundamental to speech are pathologically changed and are inadequate for the development of the complex and labile systems of connections essential for the normal functioning of speech. Consequently the speech connections of the [mentally retarded child cannot play this active role in the formation of his mental activity and the regulation of his behaviour.

The disturbance of the participation of speech in the formation of complex mental processes and the defect in its generalizing and regulatory function is a basic feature of the mentally retarded child.

CHAPTER 7

PECULIARITIES OF VERBAL ASSOCIATIONS IN CHILD-OLIGOPHRENICS

1. *The Study of Verbal Associations in the Normal and Mentally Retarded Child*

We have examined the more important problems of higher nervous functioning of the normal and anomalous child. We have seen how the general dynamics of the nervous processes of child-oligophrenics are distinguished and what part speech plays in the regulation of such a child's behaviour. Now we can transfer to the analysis of the peculiarities of the speech processes themselves in the mentally retarded child. By this means we can aspire to a scientific analysis of the bases of his thinking.

We have already noticed that discrimination and generalization are fundamental for thought processes. In order to think, it is necessary to be able to discriminate now some and now other signs and attributes of objects. If we are not able to discriminate mentally the quality of solidity, the quality of malleability, the capacity to conduct electricity or the capacity for oxidation, we will never penetrate more deeply into the nature of iron than our direct perception allows.

However, the discrimination (or in other words, abstraction) of appropriate signs is only one of the fundamental operations of cognition. A second and equally important operation is generalization or systematization. When we discriminate the property of malleability in iron, we associate this property with copper, silver, and gold and in spite of their external differences we can refer them to the single class of metals. When we discriminate the capacity to conduct an electric current we refer iron to the class of good conductors. When we discriminate the fact that iron can be oxidized and rust, we distinguish iron from the non-rusting noble metals. As a result of our minds' capacity to generalize objects with diverse appearances and to refer them to a single category on the basis of a certain property precisely discriminated, we are able to operate not only by simple visual perceptions and presentations, but also by complex discriminated *concepts* from which we can draw conclusions about the many attributes possessed by the objects included in the given category. These concepts can be transmitted from generation to generation and the understanding of them is the means of transmitting experience common to mankind. It is the essence of the process of educating the school-child and is a most powerful factor in his development.

There was a time when abstraction and generalization were considered to be the basic and primary attributes of the human soul and the fundamental innate attributes of human thinking. However, the development of science showed that discrimination and generalization, as they exist in man, are products of his social activity, his labour, and most important, of his language.

When a man calls an object "a stick" or "a stone" and uses this word for communication with other people, he is discriminating the essential attributes from the objects named and is generalizing them into well-known categories. Thus, the word "stick" can be applied to all sticks however long they are and regardless of the type of wood from which they are made. In the same measure the word "stone" refers to all stones of any colour, shape, or dimensions, but a bent wire cannot be called "a stick" and a piece of metal cannot be called "a stone". Words formulated during the many thousands of years of humanity's history preserve mankind's experience and are the weapons of abstraction and generalization which a child masters in the course of communication with adults and in his school education.

However, language does not consist entirely of separate isolated names. It consists of groups and families of words, differing in their closeness to each other and connected by bonds of different strength.

For anyone who hears the word "gold" (zoloto) other names close in meaning will immediately appear among his ideas: "silver", "metal", or "jewels", "money", etc. Rarely, however, for some normal person who has heard the word "gold" a completely irrelevant word association may occur, for example, "glue" or a word similar in sound "cold" (kholodno). The latter may occur in particular cases, for instance, in a poet who is searching for a rhyme or alliteration with this word.

It is a fact that every word we hear carries with it a whole complex of more or less rich connections partially determined by the family of words in the language in which the word is and partially dependent upon the associations based on past experience which it evokes. Because of the system of connections containing words, these connections can be the source of information diverse in breadth and width: the level of a man's intellectual development can be successfully evaluated by the richness, complexity, and depth of the sense connections excited in him by appropriate words.

We have already said above that the mentally retarded child is characterized primarily by the fact that he receives very sparse information from the external world, by the fact that the range of ideas he can deploy is very limited and that the connections dominant in his consciousness are very concrete. As we have already indicated above, the under-development of discrimination and generalization, is a fundamental characteristic of the mental life of this group of children.

Every teacher is well aware of this deficiency in the mentally retarded child which creates one of the basic difficulties in education and greatly complicates the process of the acquisition of new knowledge. However, it is not always clear what exactly lies at the root of the defect nor what characteristics of the mental life of these children need to be kept in mind for making a better analysis of their possibilities.

It might seem that it is sufficient to ask the mentally retarded child questions to uncover which sense connections dominate his consciousness, which associations arise when he hears a certain word or performs a mental action.

In fact this is far from being so. The mentally retarded child is unable to analyse himself and is incapable of giving the characteristics of the flow of his ideas. He cannot say what comes to his mind when he pronounces a certain word. It proves to be very difficult to investigate the detailed flow of the associations of the mentally retarded child.

For the teacher who wants to find out something about the sense connections which the mentally retarded child can deploy it only remains to observe the difficulties which arise in the course of education and to guess at the defects basic to these.

We will dwell here on two series of investigations which uncover the facts with the aid of objective methods, facts which have remained inaccessible for a long time.

In the first of these investigations involuntary vascular responses were used as a method of analysing the structure of the sense connections. In the second, voluntary and speech responses were used to the same end.

Initially we will dwell on the first of these.

We have already said above that every new stimulus evokes from the experimental subject an orientation response which is manifested in the following ways: a constriction of the blood vessels of the hand, a galvanic skin response etc. After the stimuli have been repeated many times in succession, they cease to attract the attention of the subject and the orientation response disappear.

This fact was utilized to subject the system of sense connections which the experimental subject deploys to an objective analysis.

Diverse words repeated several times are presented to the child undergoing investigation. He does not have to respond to these words with any responses. At first the word evokes an orientation reflex from him which is registered as a constriction of the blood vessels of the finger. Subsequently the orientation responses are extinguished.

Then the experiment transfers to the next stage, which becomes the point of departure for studying the sense connections.

One of the words whose associations will subsequently be the object of investigation is made "the signal". The child is asked to press a button every time he hears this word. Naturally this word begins to attract his attention and evoke an orientation reflex.

At this stage of the experiment no words presented to the child evoke orientation responses, but only the one word, for example "cat", which is connected with the motor response and evokes a constriction of the blood vessels of the finger each time it is presented (see Fig. 27).

If the word "cat", which we have artificially separated from all other words, evokes vascular responses, do other words connected in meaning with "cat" possess the same property?

We will test this by presenting to the normal child of junior school age words similar in sound to the word "cat" (koshka), for example, "crumb" (kroshka), "roof" (kryshka), "window" (okoshko) etc. In response to all these words the child does not have to press the button with his hand. Particularly important is the fact that these words do not evoke vascular responses from him. The similarity in the sound of these words is not sufficiently significant for the child to pay attention to it. The connections defined by the similarity in the sound of these words are inhibited in the normal child.

A quite different picture is given if we present the child with words which are similar in *sense* to the discriminated word "cat", for example, "mouse", "kitten", "dog", or even a more abstract word such as "animal". In executing the instructions given him, the normal child does not react to all these words with a press on the button (he does this only when the basic word "cat" is presented). However, the sense connection existing between all these words has the following result: every time the child hears one of these words orientation responses arise. The record in Fig. 28 illustrates the situation.

When we record the vascular responses of the child to diverse words, we obtain an *objective method of exposing* the sense connections existing in the child. This method proves to be much more

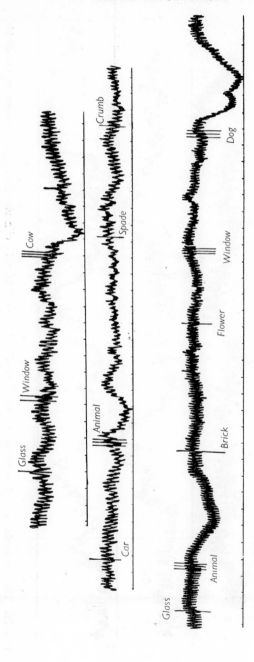

Fig. 27. The development of responses to words which have a sense connection with the signal word "cat" and the absence of responses to words which have a similar sound. The record is of a normal school child.

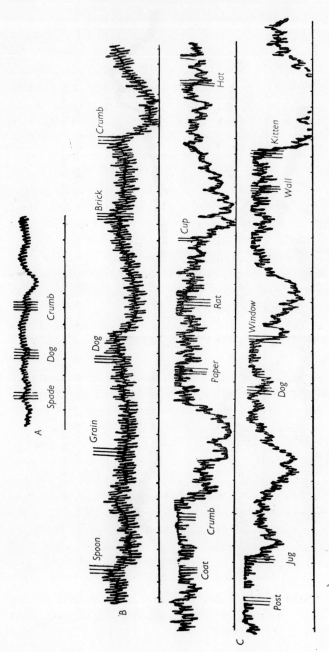

Fig. 28. The predominance of responses to words similar in sound in child-oligophrenics: A, a younger group—feeble-minded; B, an older group—feeble-minded; C, imbecility.

precise and objective than the method of direct interrogation of the child. The child asked about the similarity of the sense between the words used in the experiment answers us with difficulty. The vascular responses to the words enable us to determine the presence of these connections objectively while a measurement of the magnitude of the responses (for example, the greater intensity of the vascular response to the word "dog" relative to that to the word "animal") even affords an opportunity to measure the degree of closeness of the connection in the child.

The results of the experiments conducted show that an orderly system of sense connections is dominant in the mind of the normal child and that this repels all other connections, such as those based on similarity in sound. These prove to be insignificant. It is easy to understand the significance of the existence of this selective system of sense connections for the intellectual activity of the child.

Does this orderly system of selective sense connections exist in the mentally retarded child or do the connections typical of such a child have another character?

We can attempt to repeat the experiment just described with a mentally retarded child and we immediately notice substantial differences.

If our subject is a child with relatively mildly expressed mental retardation (a feeble-minded child), then we easily conclude that he lacks the clarity and selectivity of connections characterizing those of the normal child. As can be seen in Fig. 28, the words "mouse" or "dog" evoke the same orientation and vascular responses as the word "cat"; such sense connections are indisputably present in such a child.

However, in contrast to those of the normal school-child these vascular responses are also evoked by the presentation of words which are completely unrelated to those referring to the group of animals and have no community of sense with the word "cat" (koshka), but only a similar sound ("window" (okoshko), "crumb" (kroshka)).

This experiment shows that the clarity and selectivity of connections in the mentally retarded child lacks the characteristics of those of the normal child. The connections of words according to their external sounds are just as real as those according to similarity of sense.

In this case the excitation loses its strictly systematic character, irradiates and involves quite different connections. This experiment indicates the sources of certain difficulties encountered by the thinking of the mentally retarded child, characterized as it is by this diffuse system of connections.

The same experiment conducted with a severely mentally retarded child reveals new features.

In this case words close in sense to the basic word "cat" ("dog", "mouse") do not evoke a vascular response; this is only aroused on the presentation of words extremely close in sense to it, for example, "kitten", "tom-cat". On the other hand words close to the basic word in sound ("window" (okoshko), "crumb" (kroshka), "jug" (kruzhka), and even "cup" (chashka) or "spoon" (lozhka)), evoke the same vascular responses as the original word "cat" (koshka). Sometimes the presentation of the similar sounding word evokes, not only the involuntary vascular response, but even a press on the button, which only the basic word should evoke—according to the instructions.

Thus the system of connections characterizing the thinking of severe oligophrenics is sharply distinguished from the system of connections dominant in the normal child. Similarity in sense, which is normally very wide, is constricted. On the other hand similarity in sound, which plays no part in the cognition of the normal school child and is inhibited by the real sense connections, emerges as the primary scheme.

With an imbecile a word does not evoke a clear and selective system of sense associations, but leads to a diffuse arousal of all words similar in sound but having no sense connection with the basic word.

The experiments we have conducted with an objective analysis of the system of sense connections enable us to trace their dynamics as well as to describe their peculiarities.

We will illustrate this with two examples. It is well known

that improvement in thinking process is related to practice, but it is difficult to detect and measure this objectively. Our experiments enable us to do this within known limits. The record in Fig. 29 illustrates such an example.

The usual experiment just described was performed with a boy pupil with a relatively mild form of mental retardation. He showed the absence of orientation responses to words similar in sense and the presence of such responses to words similar in sound typical of a mentally retarded child. However, after appropriate explanatory work and the consolidation of the basic conditioned connection the same experiment conducted some time later revealed noticeable improvements. By this time the words similar in sense rather than those similar in sound began to evoke the vascular response.

However, the effect of exhaustion acting in the opposing direction is as well known as the effect of practice. Very frequently the content of the material given to a pupil is easily understood during the first lesson but is quite beyond him in the last lesson. We give an illustration of this fact in Fig. 30.

Clear orientation responses to words similar in sense to the basic word "cat" can be seen at the beginning of the school day in a school child with a relatively mild form of mental retardation. Such responses are much more rare to words similar in sound. However, the character of the responses is unstable when the same experiment is repeated with this pupil during the last lesson. Then, as can be seen from the figure, vascular responses to words similar in meaning are absent and they are aroused only by words similar in sound. Five hours of study in class results in the stable system of sense connections ceasing to be accessible to him and the level of his mental functioning drops.

Is it impossible, however, to influence the character of the connections of the pupil within certain limits and to evoke a system of more full-value sense connections from him? We will demonstrate the possibility of this with one example.

A child-imbecile in our experiment did not manifest a stable system of sense connections and reacted to a word similar in sound

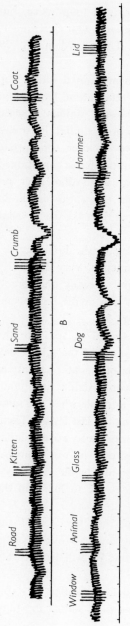

FIG. 29. The effect of strengthening sense connections in the course of an experiment: A, before consolidation; B, after strengthening.

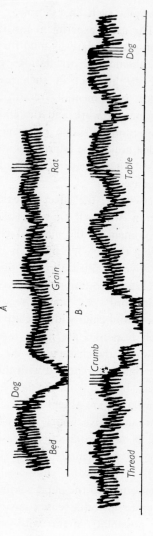

FIG. 30. The effect of fatigue on verbal connections: A, before lessons; B, after lessons.

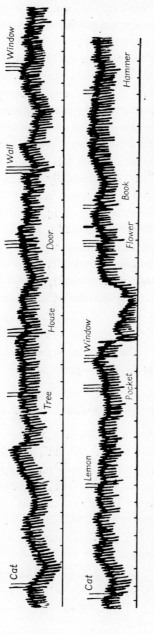

Fig. 31. The effect of the sense of the context on the responses of a child-oligophrenic (explanation of a word within a text).

to the basic word ("window" (okoshko)) with a pronounced vascular response. Cannot we inhibit this incorrect connection?

We can do this if we use certain methods of training. Every teacher is well aware of the role played in teaching by the discrimination of a word by its appropriate sense context. This method enables us to consolidate the sense and meaning of a word and inhibit extra-contextual connections inappropriate to its meaning.

We will try to apply this method. We can introduce the word "window" into a defined sense context. We can present our subject first with the word "house" (which has no similarity in sense or sound with the word "cat" and certainly evokes no vascular response). Then we can present the words "wall", "door", and finally the word "window" (okoshko). As Fig. 31 shows this method leads to clear results. While "window" (okoshko) initially evoked the same response from the mentally retarded child as the basic word "cat" (koshka) because of its similarity in sound, later, when introduced into its correct sense context, it loses this insignificant connection and ceases to evoke the incorrect response.

This example shows that correctly structured teaching can successfully overcome the incorrect directions of connections, and conversely it can stabilize those sense systems of the child on which he must base his subsequent work.

2. *A Study of the Concepts of Mentally Retarded Children*

We have dwelt on the data which enable an objective investigation of the verbal connections of the normal and mentally retarded child and we have shown the serious pathological disturbances characterizing these connections in the mentally retarded state.

Naturally the character of the connections distinguishing the thinking of the children we are studying unavoidably makes their scholastic functioning difficult, since this always requires from the pupil clarity and selectivity of the system of generalization which he can deploy.

The following important problem arises for us: how we are to study with objective methods the systems of connections lying at the root of concepts in children varying in the degree and peculiarities of their mental retardation.

The child's classification of objects, pictures, and words gives one method for a psychological investigation of the peculiarities of the concepts and processes of abstraction and generalization in mentally retarded children. The inclusion of an object in a certain category or its exclusion from it and an analysis of the attributes by which the inclusion and exclusion proceeds gave the psychologist material for determining the characteristics by which the complex processes of abstraction and generalization in a particular child take place on the basis of the use of knowledge accumulated in his past experience (L. S. Vygotskii, E. Weigl, K. Goldstein).

However, these experiments were left with an insufficient analysis of the neuro-dynamics. It remained unclear exactly *what* aspect of the defects in the analytic-synthetic process was determined by the factors of structural peculiarities of the connections and by the deficiency of the structure of the concepts themselves. It remains unclear just *what* the consequences are of the dynamic factors which lead to the exclusion of speech from a participation in the complex systems of analysis and synthesis.

In order to come closer to the solution of this problem special work was done, in which the peculiarities of the responses to verbal stimuli related to a certain general category were studied. We will show the manner of the investigation by concrete examples. We present a child with a series of words naming trees ("oak", "birch", etc.), in response to which he has to press a bulb with his *right* hand. After this we present another series of words naming animals "wolf", "cow", etc.) and in this case he must press the bulb with his left hand. Alternatively we could conduct another experiment: we could tell the child to press a rubber bulb with his right hand when the words refer to *live* objects and with his left hand when the objects were *not alive*.

With the aid of preliminary instruction, demonstration, and frequent repetition such a system of responses can be established in the majority of mentally retarded children. They begin to react correctly with one hand to the names of trees and with the other to animals.

The impression might be obtained that the mentally retarded child is classifying the words correctly referring them to different groups in accordance with their conceptual affinity. However, special investigations show that this is not so. The aroused system of connections is externally similar to the analogous system of connection in normal school children but in mentally retarded children it has certain deficiencies.

While normal children and children with delayed development can easily formulate this system of responses in a general rule of action, child-oligophrenics cannot give a generalized formulation of the rule. This already shows that the connections established in child-oligophrenics are not systematized to the necessary degree; they do not enter into the fund of the systematized connections of past experience and are not supported by generalizations which have been formulated in speech. This can easily be proved experimentally. We can introduce into the number of words presented to the child words which come within the range of neither group (trees or animals). In contrast to the verbal stimuli belonging to the concepts used in the experiment we may call these words incidental stimuli outside the frame of reference. The non-signal stimuli used in the experiments were very diverse; some of them were quite unlike the signal words while others were similar to them in some respect.

In the first group of such words, words having no similarity with the signal words were included. For example, after responses had been established to words belonging to the concepts "tree" and "animal", we began to present the following words: "sky", "stone", "snow", etc. Words similar in sound to the signals were included in the next group. For example, after the word "pine" (sosna) the word "feeding-bottle" (soska) was presented, after "aspen" (osina)—"autumn" (osen'), after "cat" (koshka)—"window" (okoshko), etc. Words having a situational contiguity with the signal word were included in the third group—thus after the original word "bird" the non-signal but situationally contiguous word "nest" was presented etc.

These experiments were to show whether the responses of the children were constrained within the limits of the concepts given or whether they easily lost the selective character and were aroused by incidental words outside the frame of reference.

In the experiments where words similar in sound were used, conditions were discovered in which the selective responses of the child, fundamental to the inclusion of a verbal signal under a concept according to a complex of significant attributes, could change to a diffuse generalization of signals according to accidental external attributes.

In the experiments where the words used were situationally contiguous with the signal words conditions were discovered in which the child could replace the clear systematization fundamental to such high forms of generalization as conceptual generalization, with the more simple form of a generalization of objects occurring in a common concrete situation.

If the experimental subject is an imbecile and he is presented with a word unrelated to the given concepts after a system of connections examined here is established, his established system of connections immediately disintegrates. Thus after a habit of pressing with the right hand in response to the names of trees and of pressing with the left hand in response to animal names had been established in Svetlana S., she reacted correctly for some time with the right hand to the words: "oak", "birch", "pine", "aspen", "fir" and with the left hand to the words: "wolf", "tiger", "horse", "dog", "bull". The impression could have been created that the subject had generalized the words presented to her completely correctly, including those under the concept "tree" in one case and with the concept "animal" in the other. When she was presented with the word "sky" she first reacted to it with one and then with the other. After this she also reacted to the signal words presented to her with two hands. The second presentation of the word "sky", after the restoration of the correct responses, also evoked a dual response and subsequent mistakes.

The introduction of a non-signal word leads to somewhat different results with feeble-minded children. Thus a differential system of responses for the left and right hands to words coming under the concepts "tree" and "animal" were established on Boris B., an excitable feeble-minded in the 3rd class.

The first presentation of the non-signal word "sky" was accompanied in this child by responses from both hands. Succeeding verbal signals also evoked dual undifferentiated responses. However, in contrast to children with severe mental retardation in this child the restoration of the differential movements to the signal words occurred spontaneously and did not require additional direct reinforcement. Although the second presentation of this word was accompanied by a dual response, it did not disrupt the differential responses to the following stimuli. Later presentations of the non-signal words did not evoke mistakes. The investigation of other feeble-minded children showed that the first presentation of the non-signal word always evokes a disruption of the differential system of responses to initial succeeding signal words. However, in some of them (excitable children) correct responses were restored spontaneously, but in others (inhibitory children) they were restored only after one or two reinforcements of the signal with the words, "It was necessary to press".

In this way, the established system of differential responses to verbal stimuli, related to two different concepts, is not complete and stable in child-oligophrenics. A small increase in the complexity of the problem, consisting of a requirement to discriminate a third category of stimuli not related to the signals but united by two concepts, evokes considerable difficulties in many child-oligophrenics. This discrimination of a third category is completely impossible for child-imbeciles: non-signal stimuli generalize unspecifically with the signals leading to a disruption of the established system of connections such that this system has to be re-established by direct reinforcement.

In children with a lesser degree of mental retardation the presentation of non-signal words also had a noticeable inhibiting effect on the established system of responses. However, the inhibiting effect was overcome in the course of the experiment.

Children with insignificant delays in development and normal children made no mistakes in these experiments.

How do mentally retarded children react if they are presented with words similar in sound to the signal words but with no common concepts with them, after a system of concepts has been established?

When the subject Svetlana S. (with severe mental retardation) was presented with "autumn" (osen') after the word "aspen" (osina) she reacted first with one hand and then with the other. The signals to which an inhibitory differentiation had been established, also began to evoke responses. The precise responses to the positive signals were also disturbed; the girl began to react to all signals with both hands. Later on in the experiment, in spite of the frequent repetition of the presentation of these signals the generalization to the word "autumn" (osen') presented after the similarly sounding signal word "aspen" (osina) could not be overcome.

The same was observed in children with severe mental underdevelopment, but in contrast to the case just examined, these had a dominance of the inhibitory and not of the excitatory process. When verbal stimuli similar in sound to the signal words were introduced into the experiment, there was also a generalization of these words with the signals, but in this case there was a subsequent reduction in the magnitude of all motor responses, leading at first to the omission of individual responses and then to the disappearance of all responses.

In this way, the use of words similar in sound evoked a generalization to the stimulus of the signal word. This generalization brings with it a disruption of the established system of connections. When the stimulatory process is dominant this disruption is expressed in the appearance of reactions of one or the other hand to every stimulus and then in the appearance of many inter-signal responses. When the inhibitory process is dominant the disruption of the system of responses is expressed in their omission and then in the inhibition of all responses.

In other children with less severe mental retardation the use of words similar in sound to the signals—in contrast to the children discussed above—does not lead to the disruption of connections already discussed but results only in temporary mistakes in reactions which are rectified by the subject himself.

In children with insignificant delays in development the use of words similar in sound to the signals evoked incorrect responses only in the first trials of the conflicting stimuli. However, these responses were always noticed by the subject to be incorrect and did not lead to mistakes in responding to the signal words.

All this strongly contrasts with the results of studying pupils in the ordinary schools. The use of stimuli similar in sound to the signal words did not evoke any disruption of the established system of responses in these children. Only preparatory movements of the hand were observed during the first presentations of these signals and these did not occur if the presented stimuli were not similar in sound to the signal words. Normally in the experimental conditions these movements were never completed as motor responses. The initiated movement of the hand towards the bulb was always inhibited before the completion of the response. This means that a signal similar in sound is to some extent conflicting even for normal children.

However, the initiated excitation is normally overcome and inhibited by the selective systematic diffusion of the stimulatory process lying at the root of conceptual generalization.

Thus the deficiency in child-oligophrenics of the established system of responses to verbal stimuli related to a common concept is manifested in these experiments by the fact that verbal stimuli similar to the signal words only in external respects enter into the system of signals of these subjects as well as words related to the concept.

This means that the deficiency of the established system of connections in child-oligophrenics is expressed in that this system does not represent a genuine system of stable selective connections. These connections co-exist with diffuse irradiation which disrupts the selective system of connections under conditions of conflict.

How will the mentally retarded child react if the words presented as non-signal stimuli are situationally contiguous to the signal stimuli?

It is known from teaching practice that mentally retarded children can easily replace a conceptual generalization by a generalization of objects according to their situational proximity. Systems of temporary connections formed in a man's past experience are fundamental to the processes associating situational proximity as well as to the processes of conceptual generalization. However, a real difference does exist between the system of connections fundamental to concepts and the system of temporary connections united by their proximity in a situation. The close proximity of objects in a situation is primarily a direct spatial and temporal closeness of stimuli perceptible in some form of concrete practical activity. The conceptual community of objects is always an indirect generalization of stimuli with abstraction from the direct closeness and similarity of them. Conceptual generalization is the indirect synthesis by a word of stimuli which may not possess spatial, temporal, or any other direct similarity.

Conceptual community relies basically on a greater complexity and a higher organization of the systems of connections, formed as a result of finer analysis and a more complex synthesis of stimuli than does community based on situational proximity. It is therefore understandable that the general reduction of the level of activation in mentally retarded children, the characteristic simplification of the structure of their functioning, and the disruption of the indirect role of their speech, result in disturbances of the processes of conceptual generalization which are more complex in organization, and these can be replaced by the more simple processes of situational generalization, thus disturbing the correct mode of thinking.

In experiments conducted with children with severe mental retardation (imbeciles) responses to two groups of words related to different concepts were established after protracted training.

In the course of the experiment the children were presented with words which named objects situationally close to one of the basic groups of words.

These experiments showed that the systems of connections established earlier in these children easily disintegrated.

We will give an example illustrating this disintegration of "conceptual" connections.

In the subject Yury G. (imbecile) a response of the right hand to names of edible products (bread, flour, apple, etc.) and of the left hand to names of inedible products was established. During the production of this system of responses a preliminary formulation of a general rule was given to the subject, "If I name something that is eaten, for example, 'bread', 'flour'', 'apple', then you press with the right hand, but if I name something which is not eaten, for example, 'stone', 'newspaper', 'clock', you press with the left hand." With the aid of a demonstration and repetition this system of responses was gradually consolidated in the subject and he began to respond correctly to the verbal stimuli presented to him.

In order to elucidate the attribute by which the subject was uniting the stimuli impinging on him, special experiments were conducted in which the following question was posed after each response, "Why did you press with that hand?" An extract from the protocol of this experiment is presented in Table 1.

The answers of the subject given in this table visually illustrate the replacement of the conceptual generalization by a situational generalization upon the presentation of words close to the signal word objects in spatial proximity. Given the diffusiveness and lack of precision of concepts and the weakness of the systems of the connections fundamental to these concepts, the selective character of the stimulatory process basic to conceptual generalization is replaced by a more simple system of connections which is the basis of visually-operative situational generalization.

Consequently the origin of the disruption of the selective responses does not stem from the instructions being "unstable" and quickly forgotten by the subject. It stems from the fact that the

TABLE 1

Stimulus words	Responses		The experi-menter's question	The subject's answer
	Right hand	Left hand		
Stone		+	Why did you press with that hand?	A stone is bad. You can't eat it.
Apple	+		,,	An apple is good. You can eat it.
Apple tree	+		,,	It's the tree on which apples . . . . fruits grow.
Carrot	+		,,	You can eat it. It's sweet.
Tomato	+		,,	A tomato is red . . . a carrot is red. You can eat it.
Bed (vegetable, flower)	+		,,	All kinds of fruit are in a garden and red tomatoes.
Garden	+		,,	Vegetables are there and different also . . ..
Earth	+		,,	You can sow.
Field	+		,,	You can sow these also.
Road	+		,,	There is a road in the field . . . a long one.

established systems of connections, in which the belonging to a certain concept serves as a differentiating sign, is not dominant and is destroyed by other more primitive systems.

A study of other child-oligophrenics suffering from severe mental under-development showed the same picture of disintegration of a system of responses, developed with difficulty, upon the introduction of conflicting stimuli.

As in the boy just discussed, in children suffering from a less severe form of mental retardation when there is a clash between conceptual generalization and situational generalization, the latter usually wins. However, with them the use of conflicting stimuli does not lead to a destruction of the whole established system of connections.

Thus, in analogous experiments Misha K. (feeble-minded) responded with his right hand to the names of objects spatially associated with food as well as to the names of edible objects. Thus, after the word "soup" he responded with his right hand to the words "knife", "fork". However, he did not respond with his right hand to the word "garden" when it was presented after the words "cabbage" and "cucumber". Thus a group of signals narrow in their spatial relations is discriminated from the whole system of spatially close stimuli and these are generalized by the subject to the corresponding words, while other words not so close spatially are inhibited. In contrast to severely mentally retarded children the presentation of spatially close stimuli does not bring about the disintegration of a whole established system of connections in these subjects. Such words as "stone" and "earth" following the presentation of conflicting words evoke a response with the left hand i.e. the correct response. In this way we have here only a widening of the range of words connected with the given concept. The words put in this group are not only those which name edible objects, but also those which name objects with very close spatial connections with edible objects. The discrimination between edible and inedible objects remains undamaged beyond the limits of this spatially close region.

In children with delayed development, the presentation of stimuli close in situation to the signal words can lead to incorrect responses to these stimuli, but these responses are noted by the subjects themselves as incorrect and do not evoke mistakes on later presentations.

Controlled investigations conducted using this method with pupils in ordinary schools show that closeness in situation never predominates over conceptual community and in the conditions of this method the process of conceptual generalization is never replaced by situational generalization.

Thus, with children suffering from severe mental under-development the presentation of signals close in situation, related to dif-

ferent concepts, leads in the problem of conceptual generalization to the conceptual generalization initially being replaced by
generalization according to situation, but then by a rejection of
all generalization. The system of responses established before
the test is disrupted in these children and is not spontaneously
restored. In children suffering from less pronounced mental retardation the use of these signals leads to their generalization with
the signal words. Here generalization according to the closeness
in situation of designated objects is united to conceptual systematization. Consequently, conceptual generalization in these children
co-exists with the generalization according to situation and is
not totally destroyed by the established system of connections.
Finally children suffering from delays in development, who do not
give up the task in conceptual generalization, only generalize
signals similar in situational relationships and later on the conceptual generalization becomes predominant and the responses
to conflicting signals are inhibited.

In the course of establishing the system of responses to words
related to the common concept, it is necessary for the subject
to ignore the evidence of the external similarity of the presented
word to other words. It is essential also to ignore the situational
similarity of the objects designated by these words and to stress
one or a complex of attributes by which the verbal signal must
be referred to the common concept. It is essential for him to combine stimuli according to these stressed attributes with a system
of similar signals and to unite the whole system of stimuli with
the defined response. Thus the processes of discrimination, abstraction (the separation of the sign from many others) and generalization according to these abstracted signs (the referring of a word
to a common concept) play a decisive role here.

Experiments have shown how unstable this aspect is in child-
oligophrenics. In child-oligophrenics stimuli externally similar
to the signals (in our instance verbal signals similar in sound)
and stimuli similar to signals in respect to situation enter into
the system of signals, generalized into a single concept, but are
not related to them in conceptual order.

For establishing a system of responses to words united by a conceptual attribute it is necessary for the subject *to inhibit all connections of this stimulus with others according to external similarity and situational proximity and to stress those connections which include it in a system of connections fundamental to the concept.*

However, the inhibition of these connections superfluous to conceptual generalization is immediately destroyed in oligophrenia in the presence of which all the complexes of uninhibited connections are included in the system of connections basic to the concept. In this way, at the root of this disturbance in discrimination in child-oligophrenics lies their inability to inhibit connections according to accidental external and situational closeness. The sum of these undiscriminated complexes of connections which are initially not freed by inhibition from all superfluous and accidental elements and are in this form combined in the common concept is a diffuse group of these connections and not the hierarchical system of connections necessary to constitute the structure of a concept. This union of complexes into a diffuse group without preliminary inhibition of unnecessary connections characterizes the disturbance of the process of generalization in oligophrenia.

It is just such peculiarities of systems of connections which lie at the basis of the concepts of child-oligophrenics. These peculiarities demonstrate the uniqueness of the disturbances in oligophrenia and they are associated with the defects of the analytic-synthetic processes which are the root of the disruption of discrimination and generalization in these children.

CHAPTER 8

SOME RESULTS AND CONCLUSIONS

WE have concluded our review of the investigations devoted to
the clinical and patho-physiological characteristics of the mentally
retarded child. These investigations led us close to the characteristics of several unique aspects of the mental activity of mentally
retarded children.

We saw that the mentally retarded child cannot simply be
viewed as a normal child with diminished intellectual capabilities.

The clinical and patho-physiological investigations show that
the mentally retarded child is in fact a child who experienced a
serious disease in the intra-uterine period of his development,
in his early childhood—or as a consequence of heredity. This
disease evoked pronounced pathological changes in his brain and
a gross disturbance of all his further mental development.

The data presented briefly in this book show that pathological
changes in the brain of the child-oligophrenic are clearly expressed in the electrical activity of the brain, in the peculiarities of
the dynamics of the simplest reflexes and in the higher nervous
activity. These changes result in a substantial disruption of his
abilities to analyse and synthesize signals coming from the external
world and to establish new associations. Finally these changes
lead to a substantial alteration in the role speech plays in the analysis of the external world and in the regulation of his behaviour—
or in other words, as I. P. Pavlov said so often in his later years,
in the "interaction of the two signalling systems".

All these peculiarities in the dynamics of the nervous processes
substantially differentiate the mentally retarded child from his
normal peers and from children with other forms of deficiency—

13   193

from deaf and partially deaf children (who because of hearing defects can experience considerable difficulties in their development), from neurally weak children, from children with affective disorders and from pedagogically neglected children.

Naturally a scientifically based discrimination of these groups, a reliable differential diagnosis, and a separation of symptoms associated with mental retardation, are urgently required. We must also make sure we do not confuse the mentally retarded child with any child whose backwardness is of another character and is associated with other factors. Only a scientifically based diagnostics, operating on a precise knowledge of the activity of higher nervous functions of mentally retarded children, can separate them from other types of retarded children and enable them to be sent for instruction in a special school, with justification. Naturally, the diagnostics of mental retardation have to be the result of a complex interaction of the work of the pedagogue defectologist, psycho-pathologist, and psychologist, this work centering around an effective analysis of higher nervous functioning. Only such a complex and scientifically based work—as opposed to a brief and superficial "doughy" investigation—can result in a qualitative analysis and a correctly applied diagnosis.

The clinical and patho-physiological study of mentally retarded children, which has been reviewed in this book, permits a separation of the *essential aspects* of those defects which occur in the functioning of mentally retarded children and lie at the root of their mental defects. These investigations, in the first place those concerned with the *electrical activity of the brain*, show the type of pathologically changed background against which the cortical activity of the mentally retarded children proceeds. They demonstrate the pathological character of the *orientation reflexes* fundamental to active mental functioning, demonstrate that these reflexes quickly extinguish, show the difficulty of making them reliable and stable and of raising them to the level of a lasting orientating-exploratory activity.

Every pedagogue appreciates the importance these scientifically established facts have for the understanding of defects in the duration of attention and the uniqueness of the functioning of the mentally retarded child.

Further, the investigations showed the severe impairment in the dynamics of the nervous processes of the mentally retarded child and the difference between their dynamics and those of the normal child. They convince us that the mentally retarded child, although easily establishing individual simple associations, is unable to form and maintain a complex system of associations, is unable to discriminate (abstract) any indirectly and slightly noticed indication that one stimulus differs from another and is unable to hold a complex relationship between signals when this relationship has been essential for some one or other task. They convince us of the difficulty with which he forms complicated associations including a whole complex of signs, of the easiness with which these systems disintegrate into their separate elements, become particular and simple, replacing isolated details with separate responses.

Psychologists and pedagogues are well aware of the difficulties the mentally retarded child experiences in cognitive activities and these difficulties are related to the mechanisms just described.

Investigations show further that there is a considerable disturbance in the *lability* of the nervous processes in the mentally retarded child. Many facts reported above enable us to see that the learned set of responses of the mentally retarded child displays a *pathological inertness*, becomes sluggish and is not easily amenable to any alteration. The sluggish "lability" of the mentally retarded child is well known to every pedagogue defectologist. It is difficult to teach them anything, but it is much more difficult to re-teach and change knowledge and habits already acquired so that they can come to have a versatile variability responsive to changing circumstances. All this is explained by the pathological change in the lability of the nervous processes—one of the foremost characteristics of the mentally retarded child.

It is known that every cognitive activity of the normal child is to a great extent *mediated by speech*. Every manifestation of reality is refracted through the prism of the complex system of

13*

verbal connections enabling the child to assimilate general human experience and to apply this to his perception of the encountered environment. Every action is regulated with the close co-operation of these verbal connections, helping the child to analyse the motives for his actions, to select necessary courses and modes of behaviour and to evaluate his actions.

With the mentally retarded child it is quite different. The investigations have shown that the very meaning of words for him is incomparably more scanty and elementary. His power of abstraction is much less efficient, his vocabulary does not systematize the manifestations of the external world into the categories which are so clearly apparent in the perception of every normal school child. The mental (semantic) associations of the mentally retarded child are much more spontaneous and primitive and develop on the basis of a vocabulary system which is much less stable.

On the other hand the nervous processes fundamental to speech functions possess much greater pathological inertness than those associated with motor activities. Naturally speech processes play a much smaller role in the organization of the activity of the mentally retarded child than that of his normal peer; his actions more easily cease to be mediated by verbal connections, escape from verbal control, and assume a spontaneous impulsive character.

The facts showing the considerable structural simplification of the behaviour of the mentally retarded child have much significance for the understanding of the psychological peculiarities of the mentally retarded child's behaviour and every pedagogue who wishes to analyse the real dynamics of the mental processes of the mentally retarded child further will draw the necessary conclusions from the facts.

All these facts comprise the physiological bases of the disturbances in the cognitive functioning of the mentally retarded child, which result in a gross disorganization of analysis and synthesis, of discrimination and generalization, and which are so well known in psychology and pedagogy. The study of these facts constitutes a real step forward in our knowledge of the basic mechanisms underlying them and enables a better understanding of the principles governing them. In this also lies the significance which the study of the clinical and patho-physiological peculiarities of the higher nervous activity of the mentally retarded child has for psychology and pedagogy.

The facts just pointed out characterize clearly the fundamental symptoms of the higher nervous activity of that group of mentally retarded children which needs to study in special schools, and they sharply demarcate this group from other types of anomalous development.

It would be incorrect to think that mentally retarded children (child-oligophrenics) form a homogeneous undifferentiated group and that it is not possible to find different degrees of defect and different types of disturbance.

In the material presented in this book there are a sufficient number of facts demonstrating the varied gradation of retardation—children with the slightest defect (feeble-mindedness) and children with a grossly pronounced degree of deficiency (imbeciles). Just as the degree of defect of the integrative nature and lability of the nervous processes, so the extent of the under-development of the system of verbal connections and the degree of the disturbance of their participation in the regulation of activity clearly differentiates these children and in both cases pose different problems to the pedagogue. Not less distinct are the other, but this time qualitative differences, which sharply set off one child-oligophrenic from others with different types of defect.

As has already been stated, the pathological changes of brain functioning can proceed differently in varied cases of injuries. In certain cases it proceeds against a background of the relative preservation of the dynamics of the vascular and cerebro-spinal fluid systems and is not accompanied by obvious symptoms of hydrocephalus. In these instances the balance of excitatory and inhibitory processes may be preserved and these children can retain the general details of sufficient equilibrium of behaviour in spite of defects in their higher nervous functioning.

In other cases the basic defect in brain activity is accompanied by a pronounced disturbance of the cerebro-spinal fluid and noticeable manifestations of hydrocephalus (water on the brain) emerge. This pathogenic factor leads to important manifestations of "weakness" and to the destruction of the balance of excitation and inhibition which, as an additional feature, noticeably changes the behaviour of mentally retarded children. As was shown above in certain children (we will call them the first sub-group) this peculiarity shows itself in their pathological excitability. They respond to every difficulty with general excitation, cannot contain themselves within the limits of organized behaviour and become restless, noisy and unorganized children for whom all forms of regulation of behaviour entail clear suffering and who consequently complicate the work of the class (in school). It is completely natural that the most important additional problem with them is to strengthen their inhibitory processes and to train them in complex forms of behaviour regulation.

The children of the second sub-group present a quite different picture. The level of their excitatory processes is too low and the processes of the overflowing (preventative) inhibition very quickly begin to predominate over those of excitation. These children begin to respond to every difficulty by becoming inert and indifferent and they easily stop working. They comprise that group of inert and passive children well known to pedagogues.

It is easy to see that if to the general picture of mental retardation is added the notion of the quality of the balance of excitatory and inhibitory processes, the pedagogical task, which includes increasing of the general tone of these children, in stimulating them to work and making it easy for them to do so, will be quite different in each case. It is important that a careful study of each of these factors permits an understanding of the many ways in which the complex group of mentally retarded children is distinguished and makes it easier to formulate these problems which each of these variants of the defect presents to the educator.

We would not have exhausted the contents of this analysis of defectology, which has concerned us in this book, if we did not pose the important question lying at the very first steps of this scientific study. We have in mind the question of the scientifically based forms and methods of *compensating for the defects* of the mentally retarded child.

The area of defectology concerned with mental retardation was for a long time an area in which pessimistic tendencies predominated vis-à-vis compensation for the defect and pedagogical possibilities of achieving this. Those gross and irreversible defects of mental functioning which are present in mentally retarded children suggested that no therapeutic influences could give any noticeable results and that every pedagogical influence would lead only to the most insignificant successes.

However, the work of specialists on oligophrenia and the careful analysis of the scientific bases of the defects possessed by the mentally retarded child have led to a substantial re-appraisal of the situation.

Experiments have shown that a correctly arranged system of training and instruction could accomplish a great deal—within known limits—towards helping mentally retarded children to compensate for their defects, enabling them to overcome certain pathological peculiarities of their behaviour and adapt to ordinary living conditions and to socially useful labour.

Experiments have also shown that the system of pedagogical measures, fundamental in the work of the special school, could function hand in hand with a system of medical and corrective measures, the first of these having an effect on the pathological peculiarities of cortical functioning and the second giving the child certain important ways to overcome his defects.

The medical as well as the pedagogical means of compensating for the defects of the mentally retarded child must be based on an exact knowledge of the peculiarities of his higher nervous functioning and on a clear appreciation of the forms the defect can take. The study of the natural scientific bases of this chapter of defectology is still at the very beginning and it is clearly understood that a thorough analysis of the scientifically based system of medical pedagogical and corrective work remains the task of future studies.

These studies are a most important part of this difficult but humane problem. The system of work adopted here was directed to a clinical and patho-physiological analysis of the peculiarities of the mentally retarded child and this book was dedicated to the presentation of a collated account of this work in which it occupies a modest but logically justified and necessary place.

AUTHOR INDEX

SUBJECT INDEX